Some of Millions

Some of Millions

From Breakdown to Breakthrough

Stories of struggle, strategy and survival,
compiled and edited by

Jethro Bor

The Book Guild Ltd

First published in Great Britain in 2020 by
The Book Guild Ltd
9 Priory Business Park
Wistow Road, Kibworth
Leicestershire, LE8 0RX
Freephone: 0800 999 2982
www.bookguild.co.uk
Email: info@bookguild.co.uk
Twitter: @bookguild

Typeset in 12pt Adobe Jenson Pro

Printed and bound by CPI Group (UK) Ltd, Croydon, CR0 4YY

ISBN 978 1913208 448

British Library Cataloguing in Publication Data.
A catalogue record for this book is available from the British Library.

This book is dedicated to my parents, Shirley and Mike, and older brother Joe for all their care and support before and while I put this book together.

Thanks go to my parents, aunt Veronica, friends Shaun and Tom, and Rosie, Joshua and all at the Book Guild for helping me write and edit this book, and to all those who generously contributed to it, especially Charlotte (1928–2018) and Jim (1982– 2018), who died of natural causes during the editorial process.

Contents

A serious psychosis is for many people the equivalent of, or worse than, being the victim of a devastating car crash, after which they need to rebuild their lives from scratch. Even if they are restored to full mental health, this would be a difficult and stressful thing to do. Perhaps the most important message of this book is that, after heroic struggles, it can be done.

Foreword
by Patrick Cockburn

his is an important and useful book. I thought I knew all too much about mental illness but, as I read the different stories and poems and looked at the pictures, I kept learning new and surprising things about the causes, symptoms and treatment of psychosis. I would sometimes give a start when I came across the description of an event which was exactly the same as my own experience. At other moments, what happened to others was completely different from what had happened to me and my family. These narratives are rich in raw experience and this means that they are far better at reflecting the reality of mental illness than many jargon-filled studies by psychiatrists and academic researchers. This hard-won knowledge is the fruit of prolonged struggles to survive and this is something of a survivor's guide. Where one has gone, others can follow.

It is not only those who are suffering from mental distress who will benefit from reading these stories. They bring to life the dark and frightening world of mental ill-health, which is so difficult to understand for those – even the most sympathetic – who have not been there. I do not think there could be a better way of explaining to the families and friends of a mentally ill person what has happened in their loved one's life. This is important because one point that comes across again and again in these stories is the crucial role of long term support from parents, siblings, husbands, wives and children. The closure of hospitals and greater reliance on 'care in the community' means that the burden of care has been shifted to the family and close friends. These are usually more than willing to help, but they need to know what is happening and what is expected of them: a simple and effective way of explaining this would be to hand them a copy of this book. They may be shocked by what they learn, but it will give them a clear idea of the devastating challenges facing their relative or friend.

I wish I had read these stories twenty years ago. As it was, I knew almost nothing about mental distress when my son Henry, who was attending art college in Brighton, had a severe psychosis in early 2002. He had set off to walk barefoot to Canterbury, which was his home, going by way of the seashore. He believed there were prisoners behind the concrete sea walls and sang to them. He tried to swim Newhaven estuary in midwinter and almost died in the freezing water before he was rescued by fishermen. He was sent first to the Priory clinic in Hove where he was diagnosed as suffering from paranoid schizophrenia and put on medication. I had been reporting on the war in Afghanistan for *The Independent* newspaper when my wife Jan called me over a crackling satellite phone to tell me what had happened. I rushed home from Kabul and went to see Henry in his room in the clinic. I was so relieved to find him alive and unhurt that I did not at first realise the seriousness and prolonged nature of his distress. I went back to my hotel and looked up schizophrenia on my laptop and was shaken to find that the US Surgeon-General had described schizophrenia as being to the mind what cancer was to the body.

I quickly found out more about mental distress and nothing that I was told was comforting. When I asked close friends if they knew anything about schizophrenia, I was surprised to find out how many of them knew a great deal about it because they had relatives affected by it. I knew many of these people well, but they had never told me about the 'madness' of a family member, probably because this was still something that people did not talk about openly. One motive for this was a belief that their relative might be stigmatised and isolated. But I came to believe that the real reason was fear: people are terrified of mental distress today in a way that they are no longer frightened of physical disease, with the possible exception of brain cancer and HIV. This terror may be dissipating as people begin to be more knowledgeable about mental distress, but it is a long way from disappearing and there is, after all, a good deal to be frightened of. Again, this book will fulfil a useful purpose if it informs people about the reality of mental distress and the challenges faced by those who are trying to cope with it.

Mental health professionals will also benefit from reading a series of narratives about what the treatment of mental distress is like from the point of view of their patients. Some will feel that they have heard it all before, but I was struck reading the stories that so many of the mistakes made by doctors and hospitals, that Jan and I had identified when Henry was being treated, turn out to have been experienced by others. For instance, doctors frequently demanded that he show 'insight' by admitting that the visions and voices that he saw and heard existed only in his imagination. He refused to do so because he said that to him they were quite real. 'Anne', one of the authors in this collection, had a similar experience when interviewed by researchers who asked about her 'manic symptoms', such as visions and voices. "I tried to explain that they were NOT imaginary but something I felt the brain actually produced," she recalls. "A comparable image is an amputee still feeling pain in the missing limb, not very easy to understand if you have not got a missing limb nor have ever been psychotic." It would be difficult to put it better than that.

The management of mental distress is so difficult because the capacity to fight back is eroded by the nature of the distress itself. A person suffering from a psychosis needs a full-time representative to deal with the issues affecting them. The National Health Service has a curious but damaging habit of asking mentally ill people to take decisions about their lives and treatment at a moment when they cannot do this because they are incapacitated by their distress. Again and again, Jan and I had to cope with a complex medical bureaucracy which was not short of goodwill but lacked resources and was poorly organised. This has all been exacerbated by the disastrous run-down of the mental hospital system since the 1960s. Those who need full-time care no longer get it and their fate depends on whether or not they have an extended family network with the understanding and resources to fill the gap.

Henry began to get better after five years in hospital when he started to take his medication rather than spitting it out, wrote a book with me about his experiences, and went back to university to complete his degree. The medication was essential to control his symptoms, but for several years – we did not realise this until late in the day – hospitals did not take practical measures to make sure he took the pills by giving them to him in soluble form and sitting by him for half an hour to ensure he did not sick them up. When his mental condition did improve, he became all the more aware that his life had been capsized at the very moment that his school friends were getting their first jobs and getting married. A sense of failure, and the knowledge that life was passing him by, depressed him. A purpose of the book we wrote and was published in 2011 – *Henry's Demons* – was to bring success back into his life and in this, as a bestseller in Britain, it largely succeeded. Henry found it much better for his self-confidence to be respectfully interviewed by the BBC or questioned by a member of the audience at a literary festival than anything said to him by psychiatrists whom he generally found to be patronising and whose control over his life he resented.

It was a psychotherapist, nevertheless, who told Henry that what 'he needed in his life was not therapy but structure'. This decided him to go back to university, no longer in Brighton but at the University of Creative Arts at Canterbury – which gave him an incentive to get up in the morning and provided an orderly structure for how he spent his time productively during the working week. It was good for him to compete with other students who were not mentally ill, something that appealed to his competitive instincts.

Why were BBC interviewers more therapeutic for Henry than so many well-meaning mental health professionals? The most important reason was that they boosted his self-confidence at every level. I found that mental health professionals greatly underrated the importance of this. 'John', in his story, sees this very clearly, remarking that 'one thing that has surprised me is the almost total lack of assertiveness/confidence building courses for people with mental health problems'. After all, a serious psychosis is for many people the equivalent of, or worse than, being the victim of a devastating car crash, after which they need to rebuild their lives from scratch. Even if they are restored to full mental health, this would be a difficult and stressful thing to do. Perhaps the most important message of this book is that, after heroic struggles, it can be done.

We want these stories to show how we are 'some of millions', to paraphrase what Sinead O'Connor recently said. We have struggled with mental distress, developed strategies and survived.

Introduction

In this book we give an insight into what it is like to live with a range of mental health challenges. We have diverse social backgrounds, ages and histories, and we have struggled with various symptoms arising from bipolar disorder, psychosis, anxiety disorder, paranoia and clinical depression. Our experiences of mental distress include deep sadness, delusions (sometimes of grandeur, or misjudgements), social anxiety, hallucinations – auditory and visual (such as hearing voices and seeing things others cannot see). Some of us have been or are challenged by the demands of basic mental or physical tasks, have had difficulties socialising, or at worst, had suicidal thoughts.

The trigger for our mental distress may have been due to sudden crises and/or gradual build up. Experiences in childhood and youth, homelessness, poverty, drug misuse, work-related stress, bereavement, and hormonal transitions such as the menopause can all leave their mark. The roots of mental illness can be social, emotional and/or biological.

These stories expose some of the shameful shortcomings in the mental health care system and provide suggestions for improvement.

We hope this book deepens your understanding of some

of the range of issues surrounding mental distress and shows some of the things that people can do to help. Our collective experience of madness and sadness varies. We want these stories to show how we are *some of millions*, to paraphrase what Sinead O'Connor recently said.[1] We have struggled with mental distress, developed strategies, and survived. Our stories are told through narratives, poetry, and artwork.

Due to the social stigma, some names used in the narratives have been changed. Medications are written beginning with capitals for drug brands and with small letters for drug types. There is a glossary of mental health conditions, medications, relevant people, organisations and mental health terms, as well as a short list of useful books and websites at the end of the book.

---

1.   www.youtube.com/watch?v=_Yv8Tm8UGcw

Narratives, Advice and an Interview

Having written all this, past
worries are fading from my mind.
I have a busy programme of
mosaic-making to work on.

'Bird' by Charlotte

Charlotte's Story

As I have long considered myself a level-headed person, to discover I was manic-depressive, or with 'bipolar disease' as they say these days, came as a considerable shock. I am now dependent on lithium and Effexor, which keep a lid on my anxiety. My story here is of a decade ago when I experienced a horrendous low, preceded by an at times elated high.

I had had a very happy holiday after which I remained positively energised and found I needed less and less sleep. Delighted by this, I couldn't understand why it worried my husband Colin and our adult children. I continued to travel a lot, develop my mosaics apace, and found I was greatly moved by music and beauty. I was very active.

Colin and my sons told me to rest, to not do so much. What seemed sensible to me did not seem so to others. Colin was particularly perturbed by my wish to sell the 'family silver' and get all sorts of things, as he had been told such behaviour was a common condition of mania in older women. I thought that that was not my style. Unperturbed, I rose early in the morning, and when on holiday enjoyed swimming before breakfast. But then when holidaying with my son Gideon and his family I became tired, tired, tired. I saw my sister Agatha who said, "I think you are very very sick," meaning that I was ill and needed help. My husband and I visited a book fair in Paris, where I began struggling with food. Everything tasted far too salty. After this it seemed to be downhill all the way.

I lost my appetite. This worried Colin as normally I am so greedy. It got worse and worse until I could not bear to eat. When home I found I could not drive of my own volition. This meant giving up my Early Risers Swimming; another £100 down the drain, as I had just renewed my membership. I now depended on Colin for journeys – seeing the doctor, shopping, visiting. During this time I found my neighbour Elisabeth to be calmingly reassuring, a true friend. She found time for me in her busy magistrate life, so I got to know her much better.

I began to worry more and more about all sorts of things, primarily I think, our finances and my sons' finances. (I thought for example that they were all getting to the age when a bright younger generation would oust them from their good positions.) Colin got really annoyed by my talking money to every Tom, Dick and Harry but realised that I somehow could not help it. I was feeling more and more tired, dreaded being alone. This eventually got so bad that I was terrified to be left alone. I was beginning to be fascinated by suicide. We had friends from America stay to see some of my husband's book collection. I lay exhausted on the green sofa. I told one of them and his wife that I was suffering from depression and playing with ideas of suicide. "Please don't do that," she said, "my sister committed suicide by hanging. It is a terrible thing for the family." She told me there were good sanatoria for depression. Colin squirmed as we had no health insurance, old age insurance, etc.

We saw a doctor, who was very kind. (Colin got round the delays in the appointment systems by saying I was suicidal.)

I was not sleeping and thought perhaps the lack of sleep was causing overtiredness and inability to cope. Various sleeping pills were tried. Apparently really strong stuff can only be given in hospital. Various treatments were explained including shock therapy (which my husband refused to consider). So we started on pills. The trouble is they take an eternity to 'kick in'. I knew I could not cope with many people coming to visit so went up to the family in London, starting with my daughter-in-law Claude who devoted a whole day to me, bathed me, massaged me, got me to eat something. I went to Gaby's, another of my sons' wives, for equal kindness. I spoke at length with an expert who had written about depressed women in Australia. My sister-in-law Nina brought me some liquid food preparation that has all the nutrients you need. My granddaughter Euphemia, four, was sweet and tried to cheer me with wise advice: "Just forget about it." She was very sad to see I was distressing her father Gideon, who I seem to remember came to sit by me when I could not sleep. Then Colin took me back home.

The telephone was a great boon. Nina and her husband John were perhaps especially interested in me as John had had severe bouts of depression, the worst one during a sabbatical in New York which should have been a care-free time. He was interested and knowledgeable about drugs. He now has his Cipramil handy. He found it excellent but warned me that a percentage of people do not find it effective (of course annoying Colin for putting doubt into my mind). Edith Morgan, a friend and former President of the World Federation of Mental Health, kept saying, "Charlotte, it will end," and had all sorts of helpful literature sent to me – except that I could not cope with it.

I became incapacitated and bed-bound, getting more and more anxious about some extraordinary things. Some rats had been eating the chicken food and I was convinced they were going to make their way up by the flat roof and into the bedroom and start nibbling my feet! Somehow I thought I would have to sleep in the garden and all the villagers would mock me! When my brother-in-law Ian came to stay I asked him to turn off my computer. I did not want to see it. (My son Simon told me that one of his depressed students had thrown his computer out of the window and then bitterly regretted it months later when he was better.) I could not envisage ever being better. I was having pains in my stomach from stress and misery. The only thing that brought relief was soaking in a hot bath, then I would sink onto the bed in a Charlton Athletic towelling dressing gown. Even putting on a nightdress was too much effort. Every molehill was a mountain. I wanted to get out of everyone's hair.

Hospital

Eventually I went to a residential hospital. My secretary Carolyn helped me pack for it, remembering her own stay in hospital for her hip replacement. She decided on my clothes. I was incapable of decisions. Time often seemed to crawl. I was thankful for a large clock on the wall from which I could tell the time, even at night, without my glasses. I would wake in the night and the room would be light enough to see the clock. It helped me monitor my sleep patterns. I don't know why I had no watch of my own.

I could not operate basic mental functions. I did not seem to be able to sort out left and right. My husband later made a sign for me on my door, which solved this problem, but for several days I used the chamber pot in my room rather than using the shared toilet and risk being locked in. It was so simple really but seemed an enormous problem. I became obsessed with having no valuables around me, asking my husband to take my rings home for safekeeping.

At the hospital I was given various tests, like drawing half past three on a clock face, and was amazed at how difficult I found this and also copying shapes. I was supposed to know the date and day of the week. I had rather lost track of the days. The doctor asked me about suicide of course (and I got rather fed up with that question). He asked me if I felt I had special powers and I answered yes. (I had in mind that my husband has often told me I emanate a feeling of calm for him often just entering a room.) I don't know what the doctor made of it! Finally he asked me what I was thinking of now. I surprised myself by saying, "You are too fat for a doctor." My poor husband had to sit through my agonising performance.

On my third morning a West Indian nurse came to wake me and told me she would give me a bath. (I had rather worried about washing as the basin in my room was not very competent.) But this was luxury indeed. She was so good and soothing. She told me she had had six children by the time she was twenty-five and was sterilised and therefore fat.

Somehow the hospital really suited me. I appreciated the two gardens, one a pretty courtyard and the other more open with green grass and some beds. There was plenty of birdlife to enjoy. Unfortunately the benches were used as a safe haven for smokers who did not all use ashtrays. I tried one day to pick up all the butts – a thankless task. I was surprised by how many of the nurses smoked and were seriously overweight. They all worked very hard and often seemed tired by the end of the shifts. The changeover was quite a sacred ceremony; they would go off to a huddle to pass on the notes and we were left for perhaps quarter of an hour. There was always a schedule pinned up to show who was specially in charge of which patient.

The cleaning staff were also very good. One way or another there were plenty of variety of people to observe, talk to and interact with. There would always be temps too, found from the 'bank'. There were day patients and of course some people were discharged and new patients admitted. We were all Oldies, some looking quite normal, but many obviously odd. But even the strangest had surprisingly nice visitors and children. I got out more and walked about the greater hospital and building sites. It was an entirely different world from my normal surroundings. Okay for a stimulating while but not for too long.

The three weeks in hospital seemed like a holiday – a much-needed change. I'd been desperate to get away from anxious family. In the hospital the nurses of course had to watch me too and keep notes about my eating, sleeping, hygiene, general behaviour. I felt very safe in hospital. There was always someone there, day and night. I could cook my own breakfast of poached egg on toast. The dining room was particularly pleasant with lovely peaceful green views from the windows. Lots of bird and squirrel life to observe. We had a communal TV and watching Wimbledon was okay by me. Although I could have done with a better paper than the *Mail*. The nurses were all nice, male and female, day and night. So were the physio and occupational therapists.

At first I felt rather indignant by my low scoring in general knowledge quizzes, about things I never had known, popstars, pop music and the like. My son Noah reassured me not to worry. It was not a serious IQ test, merely to keep us busy. We played a lot of word games every day. How many words we could get in a block of nine letters, and then finally the nine letter word. A huge jigsaw puzzle was laid out in the activity room. I could not fit one single piece. There were lots of things I couldn't do, was very bad at. Mental arithmetic was another weakness. One of our two Joyces could add up the scores of our games with lightning speed. I was better at the 'Down Memory Lane' sort of discussions, could join in. We did flower arrangements of sticking Sweet Williams into that green Oasis stuff. My jar looked awfully clumsy to me, although of course praised on some pretext by our teacher, Austrian Beatrice.

There was a gym I could go to, and a therapy room, a darkened place where for an hour we had soothing music, noises of water and birds chirping, and multi-coloured lights displaying for us. It was a bit naïve but peaceful and a change. Another nice-minded idea was a special little quiet garden created by Quaker Friends. However, a garden of course needs constant maintenance and TLC, and this one was deteriorating and fast becoming a large ashtray.

At first I'd hardly been able to concentrate on the trashiest of magazine articles, but gradually I began reading again, delving into the large selection of books and magazines available. I particularly enjoyed a book by Jill Kerr Conway about the harsh Australian life. Applying myself to a sketchbook Colin brought was more of a challenge; drawing seemed out of the question. But I did a little knitting, a useless white square, which I did just as a therapeutic activity.

The one thing that could not be called luxurious was the food! It was so high in sugars and carbs! It was brought in quite early from heaven knows where and just kept warm forever. The cabbage! The daily custard! But I was lucky. My husband brought in the most delicious food, some of which he had cooked himself and presented in beautiful dishes. He really spoiled me with summer fruits, strawberries, raspberries, cherries, peaches – all the best of Waitrose! My daughter-in-law Claude came with lovely food and took me out up to the main hospital, and sorted out nice clothes for me. I could not believe she had come from London for me. Colin and our son Daniel took me out to a Thai meal. Then I got home leave, weekend leave, and finally I had my review and was discharged, ready to go home and face the world again! It had been a short sharp shock, quite pleasant, fascinating but enough!

Moving On

Once home I was very pleased to have home visiting from my CPN (Community Psychiatric Nurse), Claire. It was nice to talk at home, in our kitchen instead of hospital rooms. It meant Colin was in on the act too. We had hour-long sessions to begin with. She was very keen to encourage me to believe in myself. But in spite of her best efforts, and my own hopes that I would soon put all this depression behind me, live a normal life again and everyone telling me I was 'better', somehow I was not right.

Colin and I went on holidays that I at first dreaded, but which worked out okay. Socialising was just about all right but I did not truly enjoy it. My time in South Africa went well. I enjoyed the people, the scenery, the luxury, old friends, and the lectures. However, despite all these journeys, the change of scenery did not help shift my mood. I had vague ideas of doing some voluntary work, starting a book-reading group, going on more courses. People suggested all sorts of things but I preferred to do nothing, liked best to stay in bed, and found shopping decision-making dreadful. I even asked my granddaughter Euphemia to help me choose new glasses. I spent a lot of time watching TV. My son Gideon very kindly took this up and gave me Sky so that I would have a greater choice, which I have enjoyed, news and sport in particular – and also the grandchildren liked a lot of the programmes.

Claire suggested Cognitive Behavioural Therapy (CBT) after her consultation with the expert Philip Wilkinson. I did not fancy going a long way. But amazingly Philip was prepared to take me on himself.

The Ridgeway Centre at Didcot was where I went, a pleasant venue, easy to get to, and easy to park right there free – unlike Churchill Hospital which was a bit of a nightmare for parking. Our sessions were recorded and I found this most helpful to listen back in the car. Again Colin was interested and quite complimentary about my lucidity. CBT is a relatively recent American method and liked at Cambridge, so my son Simon tells me, because it takes a limited period. It is not just a talking cure. One is meant to contribute, do homework. This includes using visual aids such as charts, graphs and diagrams. You are supposed to schedule, write things down, plan, break up tasks.

The first surprise I got was that whereas rest is normally good, for depression it isn't! I'd been indulging myself with endless rest hoping it would get me through the other side but it never did. One of the tasks was to keep a diary hour by hour of my 'activities'. This really showed me up. So I would try and do things to have something to fill in. Having to evaluate out of ten things I had enjoyed doing was more difficult. At regular intervals I was asked to complete a 'Beck Questionnaire'. The first time was in the hospital where I just put choice (d), the worst, for all twenty questions. Colin protested that I should give it some proper thought. During this long period of convalescence my score fluctuated around mild depression.

I enjoyed my sessions and looked forward to them. I was impressed how Philip used whatever cropped up to pull it back into the theme of that session. I considered myself very lucky that my therapist and physician were one and the same. He was good-humoured and always on my side. Even when

I had not done my bit of homework, i.e. challenging negative feelings, he would be patient, not annoyed and we would work through the task together.

I made slow progress, was disappointed in myself. Colin had been wonderfully supportive, non-judgemental, endlessly patient, imaginative with suggestions of activities – and I was self-absorbed, tired, dragging on my life.

Medication

Medications often take a long time to have an effect, so it is difficult to know whether they are helping. I had mostly Specific Serotonin Re-uptake Inhibitors (SSRIs). The possible side effects include just about every unpleasantness you can possibly imagine. Effexor, for example, can cause blurred vision, fever, difficulty urinating, muscle spasm, tinnitus, hallucinations, yellow skin, bruising, and bleeding as just a few of its unintended consequences.

For a long time I had a prejudice against mood stabilisers like lithium. One needs to be monitored and have regular blood tests, and I did not like that idea. Philip suggested I might like to take part in a trial that was being organised from Oxford. In theory I thought I should cooperate and be helpful in the name of science, but I did not want to be committed for so long (although one could leave the trial voluntarily), and was somehow suspicious that it was for the benefit of the drugs companies rather than science – but had no real reason to think so. Eventually I accepted a fairly low dose of lithium, the blood tests which are really no big deal and have dropped all other medication. I rejoiced in the return of my appetite, love of food, interest in cooking, and indulged. Immediately I put on weight and have not yet had the discipline to lose it again – maybe after Christmas?

Causes

My father, who as a structural engineer, told me that major disasters to a building usually occur because of a combination of unusual circumstances. So what came together in my breakdown?

1. I accept there is a hereditary tendency for depression in our family. I have spent a lot of my life being 'tired'. Way back college friends remember me resting during the day. At intervals during my life, the doctors I went to (at least four GPs) gave me iron, Valium, and told me I had five good reasons to be tired! But nobody ever suggested depression. I thought that just as some people had above normal levels of energy, so unfortunately I had below average. My brother John and I believed we both suffered from LEP (Low Energy Problem).

2. I know that somehow I had not got rid of anger about my son Jacob's death. There had been an injustice.

3. I've had a niggle for a long time that I was not independent financially, no career of my own, stupidly old-fashioned full-time wife, housewife, mother.

4. Differences between Colin and me about old age, plans, provisions. He wanted to move further out, away from London, to a 'cottage' – if indeed we were to move at all. I wanted to downsize to something small and convenient and warm and low maintenance.

The Future

My son Gideon has come to my mental rescue by buying the bungalow next to his house in Forest Hill where he and his wife Mio have assured me of an independent 'granny flat'. Fantastic. And Mio is tough enough to get rid of me if I should prove a nuisance.

Turning to the future, Colin and I have great celebratory travel plans and I am particularly thankful that I can again enjoy the developing lives if our grandchildren, all eleven of them. Just now, as I write, we expect a full house here in our barns over Xmas and having written all this, past worries are fading from my mind. I have a busy programme of mosaic-making to work on when we get back from our travels in February.

I knew something was very wrong and sought the comfort of my paternal grandmother who lived in the countryside. She was the person in my life with whom I had always felt safe and who loved me unconditionally... She was my friend, was never judgemental and she understood.

'Echidna dreaming' by Daniel

Rebecca's Story

History

I remember my first panic attack in my twenties. I was in the bank standing in a queue and my heart started pounding and I felt faint. I had no idea what was happening and thought I was having a heart attack. This was the precursor to my first breakdown. I had suffered from depression for years. As a child I remember being in a bad mood when I woke up in the morning and picking fights with my siblings; so much so that I remember on occasions being asked to leave the breakfast table.

My parents divorced when I was seven. I suspect that my early morning anger was a manifestation of the unexpressed pain that I suffered as a result. I was, as they say, 'acting out'. I remember being confused and feeling unloved and as the elder sibling had learned from a young age to adopt coping skills which hid my pain. I was prone to sulk in my room for hours waiting for my mother to come and talk to me so that I would have the opportunity to unleash the pain – she rarely did. She was unable to disguise her hatred of my father and my loyalties were split between the two for as long as I can remember pretty much until I became a mother myself.

I remember in my teens a psychiatrist saying to me that if I didn't address my issues there could be grave consequences… He was right of course and the breakdown I suffered in my late twenties was entirely due to my ability to disguise my depression… I was basically angry and morose.

I sought a therapeutic breakthrough – however my learned behaviour of suppressing true feelings, reasonable intelligence and well-developed sense of humour meant that I was able to run rings around therapists and I protected myself from facing my demons head on. There was much debate as to whether the cause of my despondency was endogenous or reactive. Years later it became clear that my pre-menstrual mood swings were entirely down to hormonal imbalances. I have my own theories that if one is depressed for endogenous reasons this leads to negative thinking which compounds the root cause and sends one spiraling into the cycle of negative and suicidal thinking.

Breakdown

At the time of my first breakdown I was running my own business and was struggling with it. As a perfectionist – my failure to make a success of it was bringing me down and I had severe financial worries as a result. Looking back, the onset of what happened afterwards was entirely reactive to my predicament. I became unable to cope at all with any aspect of my life. I knew something was very wrong and sought the comfort of my paternal grandmother who lived in the countryside. She was the person in my life with whom I had always felt safe and who loved me unconditionally. She was also aware of the profound impact of the divorce. She was my friend, was never judgemental and she understood. She welcomed me into her home, although it was deeply distressing for her to witness the terrible state I was in. Allowing myself to admit there was a problem meant that I was able to let go and the symptoms became dramatically worse and frightening both for her and for me. She couldn't cope and eventually I ended up in a psychiatric hospital for many weeks and was prescribed anti-depressants. I remember having hallucinatory out-of-body experiences. I have no idea to this day whether those were due to the drugs I was on or the distress. I was petrified and thought I was going mad.

I remember my experiences in group therapy sessions with several extremely ill people made me feel better and changed my perspective. I underwent Cognitive Behavioural Therapy to help me with the panic attacks. Of course I was on strong meds including beta-blockers, which I didn't like at all because I wanted to get better without them. That feeling of being out of control is not comfortable for me at all. I recognise too that my experience was different to others but I am not convinced that enough is known about the psychotropic drugs that are widely prescribed to treat depressive distress and that worried me then and subsequently whenever they have been prescribed. I have always made a point of coming off meds as quickly as possible. I'm not convinced either that some anti-depressants don't have the reverse effect and may have the patient feeling worse and may indeed compound depressive symptoms.

What I realised as a result of listening to other patients talking of their own distress and experiences was that I wanted to get better (even though I worried that I wouldn't) and I found an inner resolve and strength which enabled me to become well again. I do not believe that was due to the medication (although I accept that in the acute stages of a depressive episode they may be essential). What was of far more value was the therapeutic help I received. I think I grew up not talking much about my true feelings and now I was in a situation where I could and that was of far more benefit to me than the medication, even though I was aware they had the function of dampening the acuteness of my frightening symptoms. I became more aware of my behaviour and how it affected my relationships with others. Certain breakthrough moments had me allowing myself to let go of situations that I simply could not change and which had caused perpetual frustration for as long as I could remember.

Medication

Certainly whenever I have resorted to taking any kinds of anti-depressants the side effects have been upsetting and interfered with my being able to lead a normal life. I remember crashing my car once because I was doped up on anti-depressants. In the context of my work I have found that my creative brain is foggy and impaired, and sexual feeling has been dampened. I think too that because I will always be able to recognise the warning signs of any potential acute episode having been through that terrible experience, I will always choose therapy over drugs. I appreciate that for many that may not be possible. That strength which had enabled me to suppress deep-rooted sadness was effective in taking me out of the black hole and ridding myself of the depression which had crippled me.

The Path

I don't think I would have worked as hard to sort out my life if I had not experienced such a severe and total breakdown, and it may appear strange that I am grateful I cracked up. It set me on a path of greater self-awareness and prompted me to heal myself as much as possible. I have repaired my relationship with my parents and am no longer angry with them for failing me. I accept that I will remain vulnerable to mood swings and will always tackle acute manifestations appropriately, as indeed I did when I began going through the menopause which caused massive fluctuations in my hormone levels and I felt terrible. I made the decision to address those with hormone replacement therapy rather than anti-depressant medication. I remember discussing this in depth with my GP at the time and the fact that the hormonal fluctuations were contributing to my moods made it easier to decide to correct those imbalances rather than suppress the manifestation of them with a psychotropic prescription. I have been fortunate to have been able to make decisions jointly with my doctors as to the best way to deal with my vulnerability to depressive episodes. There is no doubt either that being able to recognise the warning signs means that I can take ownership of how best to adopt the appropriate therapies to treat them before they take over my life.

I have a great support worker who always tries to encourage me and understands my experiences really well. I've also seen a psychologist for Cognitive Behavioural Therapy, which helped me understand certain aspects of my distress.

' Sax Man' by Daniel

Edward's Story

my name is Edward. I am forty-six years old with a diagnosis of paranoid schizophrenia, first diagnosed back in 1990. I will set out my history the best way I can, although there is so much I could write which is beyond the scope of one article. I will record the most important things I can remember.

Back in early 1990 I was living in London working in catering as a storeman. It was a good job, and I worked with some lovely people. Everything was good until I started to become very paranoid about the people around me, which ended up in me confronting people and accusing them of talking about me behind my back, and conspiring against me. I was also hallucinating seeing bugs in my bed, and hearing voices (which I thought was God) telling me many things, even down to which direction I should walk when I was on the street. I would talk back to the voices too. (Something I learned later was a bad idea; it made things worse.) A recurring theme over the years started then, that God was against me, and was turning the world against me. At the time I didn't know about schizophrenia, and didn't know I was ill.

The only thing I could think to do was go back to my hometown in Manchester to be with my family. I thought that might help. Unfortunately I wasn't welcomed, and went sofa-surfing where I could, ending up staying with a heroin addict (bad idea). Thankfully I bumped into someone who knew me at school, who saw what a mess I was in, and rang an ambulance. On the way to hospital I was convinced I would be thrown in a padded cell, not knowing what hospital would be like. The first thing I remember was a nurse asking me to take some medication, saying they would make me feel better. (Not true!) I was in hospital for three months taking chlorpromazine, Modacate injections and Stelazine.

Over the next two years I lived in two different hostels, not improving much at all. Every time I saw the psychiatrist he'd put me on yet more medication. Thankfully the officer of the hostel said she thought I was on a ridiculous amount of meds, and wanted to see the doctor with me to tell him his approach wasn't working. The doctor was very nice to me, saying there was a new drug called clozapine and that he wanted to admit me that day and put me on that. I agreed, and was admitted.

They took me off all my meds at once, and started me on the clozapine straight away. Unfortunately the first night I collapsed with very low blood pressure, and was monitored in bed, not being able to stand. Things improved, and I was kept on the Clozaril (clozapine). After a few months I was sent back to the hostel, and things were improving. The paranoia was more manageable, plus I was understanding myself better, getting used to my experiences and on a quest to sort things out the best way I could.

I was offered a flat, and was helped to move in. It was a big step, and I found it quite hard at first. I was so used to having support in the hostel. It was about that time (1993) that an important event occured. My mother, whom I'd not seen since 1976, managed to find me. We spoke by phone often, and I finally felt my life was improving. I'd also started some voluntary work at a day centre for learning difficulties, and was really enjoying it. I felt more like my old self again. I rang the hospital and said I wasn't taking my meds any more, as I felt I didn't need them. They warned me against it, but I wasn't listening at all. As far as I was concerned, I had more energy after stopping the clozapine, and started to believe the doctors and nurses were trying to control my life, and they had a secret agenda and wanted me dead. I was on a mission to have nothing to do with the mental health system. I would sort things out on my own.

At this time, my mother persuaded me to move down to her home in Southampton, and I eagerly agreed. This would be a new life for me as far I was concerned. I said goodbye to everyone, and moved down in January 1993. It didn't take long before my distress returned with a vengeance. I was only sleeping two hours a night, and I seemed to dream all the time I was asleep. I started to view my mother in a very negative way, believing she was knowingly behind all my experiences, causing them. Needless to say after a massive confrontation I went back to Manchester, with nowhere to live and in a very bad state. I'd lost a load of weight, and still couldn't sleep. People meeting me thought I was a junkie. The voices were getting worse, and I was having anxiety attacks.

Thankfully, a worker from the local branch of the mental health charity MIND came to my aid after me turning up for help. He took me straight to the doctors, who immediately gave me some medication, although I can't remember what it was. The plan was to put me back on Clozaril as soon as possible. Also a place was found for me in a MIND hostel. I have stayed on my meds since then. There's no way I'll try to stop my meds again. I still take them with reluctance, though.

Like a lot of people, I've had to face up to the fact that I have to live my whole life on medication.

Over the years my dose has been altered, and thanks to different doctors a decent level has been achieved. It's a balance of being therapeutic, but not too much that I'm dosed up and sleeping all day. I've also been on venlaflaxine (an anti-depressant) since about 2000, which has helped with the suicidal tendencies I've had since my late teens.

Moving back to Southampton in 2003, after regaining contact with my family there, was a major event. Since then I've managed to build a life here, and have made some good friends over the years. I've had a few spells in hospital, and things still can be difficult. I find socialising difficult at times, and still have what I call 'experiences', having to deal with feelings of threat and paranoia, and life is a struggle sometimes. I've had much better support, though, since living in Southampton. I've had some excellent doctors (and one I couldn't stand!). I have a great support worker who always tries to encourage me and understands my experiences really well. I've also seen a psychologist for Cognitive Behavioural Therapy, which helped me understand certain aspects of my distress.

I live my life day to day, and don't plan too much. What I do depends on how well I am, but I feel the worst has already happened to me.

I could have written a lot more, but hope what I have written has conveyed some of my experience of living with schizophrenia.

And also, don't give up!

Edward. x

Sessions with a bereavement counsellor... helped me enormously... I was able to talk openly and frankly... which really helped. I did cry through most of the sessions, but that actually helped me; and both counsellors made me feel at ease and reassured me that it was perfectly okay to cry during the sessions with them. I feel that did help me lots and it helped me realise that it was okay to feel emotional at times and it was important not to bottle those feelings up.

'Jungle' by Daniel

Pic's Story

When I was around eight years old I had my first episode of depression. It was quite frightening as I didn't understand what was happening to me. It would have been around 1976 so was back in a time where people did not openly discuss their mental health. Everything was swept under the carpet in those days and so was my depression.

I was taken to the doctor, given tablets, and that was that. No discussion, no questions. No helping, nothing. I had been diagnosed with anxiety and depression but it felt like no one cared or believed my feelings, so it was ignored for many, many years. My mum would describe it as one of my 'funny turns'. My mother used to get very angry with me. She often blamed me for being awkward, but I didn't understand what she really meant. I was just being me. I became frightened of people and noises and that remains to this day.

As I got older the anxiety got worse. I was given medication to calm the anxiety, but still nobody asked me how it was in my head. As I became a teenager I found ways of calming myself when I was anxious. This involved me cutting my arms and my legs. I did this in private and up until I met my husband it remained my secret.

When I was thirteen, my teacher became concerned about me and referred me to the school counsellor. I saw her regularly each week throughout my time in secondary school. When I got to my final year at school the counsellor persuaded me to let her talk to my parents so they could help me in the future, once I left school. My parents came up to the school and had a meeting with the counsellor. I was hoping it would help and that they would become supportive but they didn't. They said I was an embarrassment to them and that was that.

By the time I was nineteen, I had had several depressive episodes. My father died and I was sent away by my mother and aunt to live in a convent with Catholic nuns. My mum felt that me becoming a nun would be a 'cure-all'. Although the nuns were very kind to me I didn't want to be there. I felt isolated from everything and needed my friends. I needed to be away from the convent. After six months I rang my friend, who came to get me. It took me quite a while to readjust. Later that year I met my future husband and came back to live in London.

However, living with my mum made my anxiety worse. I began to have panic attacks. I began to have obsessions and compulsions, which I used as a coping mechanism, but it was very negative for me and made me quite ill. In 1990 I had a complete mental breakdown and spent three months in hospital and the staff weren't always kind. I had Cognitive Behavioural Therapy (CBT) and that helped me.

In 1991 I got married and moved to a different part of London, away from my mother. We had a new GP as we moved area and so I felt safe to tell my feelings. In 1994 I was struggling quite a bit with depression and anxiety again. My husband felt it was important to visit my GP with me. That day I just unburdened myself and confided in her all the things that were making me so anxious. My GP and my husband were brilliant and supportive. I had another breakdown and was hospitalised again. I went voluntarily this time and after a couple of weeks I discharged myself and went home. I was becoming anxious about being away from my husband. I visited my GP and told her how I felt. She was brilliant. It was agreed that I would be in her care. I was to see her every week and in between times, if I needed.

From then I was also sent to see a psychiatrist. I was very intimidated seeing this particular psychiatrist. He made me feel very uncomfortable. He asked very personal questions that I felt had nothing to do with my mental health. It felt strange to be asked such questions by a stranger. After all, I had never openly discussed my mental health difficulties with anyone apart from my husband. After three appointments I asked if I could terminate the consultations, as they were making me more anxious rather than helping me. This was agreed and I was referred to a counsellor. I had a few months wait till I got an appointment.

The first psychologist I saw I didn't particularly warm to and the first few weeks I just sat silently during the appointment. I just found it really difficult to speak to him. I felt almost panicked during the appointments. Eventually I was given another psychologist. This time it was an older female. I saw her once a week for over two years. It would have been longer but for her saying something upsetting to me one day. I took it very personally and stopped going to the appointments. I also felt exhausted at the time when I was talking about my earlier life. I didn't feel like talking anymore, so it suited me just to walk away. I then had a few years of being relatively well and just under the care of my GP. I continued to take my anti-depressants and all was well.

In 2012 my husband died of cancer. I had nursed him and had remained as strong as I could the whole time. Literally after the funeral my mental health spiralled downward. My husband had always taken care of me and kept an eye on my mental health, etc. So I felt secure and well-looked after. Living on my own was going to be a huge change. I began to self-harm and cut my wrists. I took an overdose and then I was admitted to hospital. I was a voluntary patient. I was told this would be the better option because if I were sectioned, I would have no choices or say in what would happen to me. This was quite frightening, as until it happened to me, I had no idea that medication could be forcibly given to you once you are sectioned.

I hated being in hospital. It was quite frightening and very noisy at times. I didn't like the noise. When I wasn't in hospital I was often under the care of the Crisis Team. This can be quite intimidating and at first I was quite fearful of being under their care, but largely they were good. The first time I was in their care I didn't like it. Everyday they would come to my home and see me. Everyday it was a different care worker and I found that quite difficult. The latter times I was under the Crisis Team. I asked for the same care worker and they made that possible. That helped me very much. When I was under Crisis Team care, I was seen by a consultant psychiatrist. She was very nice and even hugged me when I was upset. This simple gesture meant so much to me when I was so poorly. It made me feel that someone genuinely cared for me.

I am currently under the CDAT (Complex Depression, Anxiety and Trauma) Team. This involves me seeing the psychiatric team. I don't particularly like the psychiatric team as all they seem to do is give me more medication to take.

In February 2013, I was diagnosed with psychosis. At the time I was quite ill and so I just took whatever medication the team told me to take. I started off by taking quetiapine. It did help me sleep but my sleep involved me having quite vivid, frightening dreams. I didn't know until I stopped taking them that this was a side effect of quetiapine. After taking it for more than a year, I became fed up with side effects including feeling tired constantly, jerking movements, vivid dreams, etc. I decided to stop taking my anti-psychotic medication. For about two weeks I felt great. I was able to wake up properly in the morning and feel alert, but then gradually my mood went down and the hallucinations I suffered began to get more frequent. When the psychiatric team found out I was not on my medication they persuaded me to try another type of anti-psychotic. This medication was called sulpiride. This made me feel really drowsy, so I was taken off them and put on aripiprazole. This made me unable to sleep and so eventually I was put on risperidone, which I am still taking and that seems to be okay. As well as risperidone, I take 50mg of the anti-depressant Seroxat. I have been on Seroxat for over twenty years. I am now on the maximum dose. I cannot come off it as my body has become dependent on it. If I don't take it daily I start to get withdrawal and experience sickness, dizziness, headshocks, and agitation, along with panic attacks.

I have in recent times had some positive connections with bereavement counsellors. I had two lots of counselling a year apart. Each lot consisted of ten sessions with a bereavement counsellor. They helped me enormously as my mental health was very fragile at the time. I liked both counsellors very much and connected with them very easily and quickly. I was able to talk openly and frankly with them, which really helped. I did cry through most of the sessions, but that actually helped me; and both counsellors made me feel at ease and reassured me that it was perfectly okay to cry during the sessions with them. I feel that did help me lots and it helped me realise that it was okay to feel emotional at times and it was important not to bottle those feelings up.

In July 2013, I was referred to a local Day Centre. I had my initial meeting and it was agreed that I should be given a place there. I was put on a waiting list. It was over a year later when I started my first day at the Centre, in late August 2014. The Day Centre was the only place I felt I could belong. Every person there had mental health difficulties, ranging from schizophrenia, bipolar, personality disorder, to depression and anxiety.

From my first day there I felt like I belonged. People were friendly and seemed to genuinely care about each other. I liked that and made some good friends there. Part of the Day Centre structure was to take part in various activities. Alongside the activities you received therapy. I did art therapy, yoga, choir and pottery. I attended there four days a week. My days were filled with activities and therapy. There was large group therapy, which was quite difficult. After being at the day centre for a few months I withdrew from large group therapy. Then I was put in a reference group. This was small group therapy. I was one of eight people in it. Here we were encouraged to discuss our thoughts and feelings. From the very beginning I struggled in this group. Some of the things we talked about made me feel upset. As with most things, it would be difficult to start the conversations, but then you would elaborate and speak in depth. The only problem was that it would take a while to get the conversation flowing and then when you did it would be time to stop because the therapy session had ended. I found that really difficult, as my raw emotions would be on display as everyone was leaving the therapy session. Eventually I became disillusioned with talking therapy and began to resent being part of the group. I didn't want to talk anymore.

As a service user we were each given a key worker to help and care for us individually. This was a massive help especially when things in life became difficult or too much. It meant you had someone to go to who you could discuss things with and who would help sort things out. This was invaluable and was the best part of the Day Centre. I got to see my key worker once a week for an hour. A year after I started the Day Centre I stopped attending. Things were changing there. The local council were making cuts and I felt that I was getting anxious about that. I decided that I currently felt well enough to look after myself so discharged myself as a service user. Currently I am taking my medication. My mood is good. My mind is in a good place. I start an art course shortly and so my life is quite happy and stable…

A few months since writing this I became ill again and was placed in a Crisis house with the Crisis Team. I got a new psychiatrist and had a few meetings with him. I have been diagnosed with borderline personality disorder. I now also attend a new day centre run by the charity MIND.

For sufferers whose recovery is progressing well, trying to find introductory paid employment, rather than unpaid volunteering can be a nightmare. Maybe the solution is to gradually help people with mental health problems off benefits and into work by starting with a work trial with low-intensity duties, and progressing from there.

'Horses' by Gingerberry Rose

John's Story

Mental Health, Life and Me: Functioning and Succeeding

my first encounter with mental health issues came eleven years ago, when I experienced an anxiety-induced psychosis. I spent a month on an inpatient mental health unit, before being released. The psychosis was a deeply disturbing experience for me, but my period in hospital was made much easier by the kindness of one particular mental health nurse. To be honest, this chapter in my life seems like a bit of a blur now. I don't see it as a turning point in my life, as I had experienced difficulties prior to the episode. It has, admittedly, made me more sensitive to people's behaviour, as well as to the treatment of others with mental health disabilities.

However, looking at my life now, I don't see myself as entrapped by my mental health condition, and my only interaction with mental health as a concept is through medication and occasional therapy. I think the most therapeutic avenue for me during the early post-admission years was with a discussion group for people with mental health problems at my local library. We would talk about political and cultural issues, and occasionally go out for trips. It was useful to meet people whose day-to-day experiences could be described as 'foggy', and who were relatively non-judgemental and accepting. Unpaid voluntary work was also useful for me, as I was able to be in a work environment on a daily basis and therefore not be isolated. I also found therapy useful at this stage, although I don't receive it now.

So, how has my life evolved since my initial episode? Well, I have found it difficult – although not impossible – to maintain employment of any kind. My deep-seated social anxiety, combined with frequent paranoia about colleagues, have been huge roadblocks. On the plus side, I recently completed an Open University degree. The format of the OU – learning at a distance rather than campus-based – has suited me. It has given me a huge boost in self-esteem, although my general mental health is not massively different.

The main mental health symptom I suffer from is called a 'thought disorder'. These symptoms involve hearing thoughts repeatedly in one's head. Some people have thoughts based around obsessive routines, but mine tend to be about people. This makes it difficult for me to be in the outside world during these thought disorders, and I find it difficult to organise my thoughts in order to communicate, even with my parents. My family tend to find it very difficult to adjust to my symptoms, and the threat of thought disorders had forced me to stay away from family events. As far as coping strategies are concerned, my main strategy is to listen to music. It is, however, difficult to manage these sorts of symptoms effectively.

I think society is becoming more accepting of mental illness, but there are still a lot of barriers to be broken down. Talking about issues such as thought disorders in the public sphere is problematic, as they might add to the impression that mental illness can make people dangerous or socially unpredictable. Tabloid coverage is also unhelpful. The increased pace of daily life means that more than ever, first impressions count and that presents problems regarding acceptance of people with mental health issues. One thing that has surprised me is the near-total lack of assertiveness/confidence-building courses for people with mental health problems. Maybe there's a niche for such an organisation to be set up?

Do I feel different because I have a mental health problem? Well, my accompanying social problems have exacerbated feelings of difference in me. On the positive side, I have a very supportive family and I have met a lot of people through my condition who possess huge reserves of kindness and humanity. The key point is that you have to maintain good levels of confidence, and be open to trying different avenues, despite the possibility that these might fail. Also, my medication has suppressed many of my original psychotic symptoms, and I do feel a sense of stability being on it. I suppose I have been fortunate to have had relatively mild mental health problems – I haven't had schizophrenia, and my experience of hearing voices has been minimal.

One thing I would take away from my experience is that life can be rich and fun even if you have suffered from depression or psychosis – you just have to enjoy every day. My experiences with therapy have been largely beneficial. It has given me a lift in difficult times, and has made me realise that my perception of the world whilst feeling ill can be a little skewed! Therapeutic interventions are useful more broadly for mental health sufferers, especially if they are isolated or lacking in confidence. I do think though that the therapeutic environment is not always a good simulation for the pressures of the outside world.

Having supportive parents has been key for me. My dad worked in the NHS for most of his adult life, and therefore he has a lot of experience of dealing with people far more affected than I have ever been. Also, having sensitive and intelligent parents has allowed me to access wider aspects of life as a way of trying to make the best of things despite my difficulties.

While writing, other thoughts have come to mind which I'm going to discuss separately now, as I did not want to interrupt the flow of my general narrative.

1. Although I said earlier that I benefited from therapy, there are problems with it. In terms of person-to-person interaction between sufferers and NHS professionals, it is all too easy for responses in counselling to become platitudes, which leave no lasting healing, and which therefore cannot build confidence in a positive way. I've had good and bad interactions in this way.

2. The National Autistic Society – an organisation I've had lots of contact with – has a fair amount of social group initiatives. In comparison, the NHS doesn't have the same amount of similar projects for adults with mental health problems. I've often felt dumped in the long gap from one appointment to another, and this is even worse when a subsequent appointment involves professionals who haven't previously followed me through.

3. For sufferers whose recovery is progressing well, trying to find introductory paid employment rather than unpaid volunteering can be a nightmare. Maybe the solution is to gradually help people with mental health problems off benefits and into work by starting with a work trial with low-intensity duties, and progressing from there, instead of terminating support because they are found not to have severe enough disabilities. Partly this problem arises because employers have a low tolerance levels for the kinds of challenges that employees with mental health problems present.

I feel positive about my future – I know my condition is likely to remain, but I've got a degree now and can and will try to find pathways that can enrich my life. I have an accepting nature and I feel my mental health difficulties have made me even more accepting of people whose behaviour differs from the norm. I'll finish by reiterating that society needs to become more accommodating towards mental health, and the work charities and celebrities do in breaking down barriers is extremely important in facilitating a better societal attitude.

After experiencing significant mental trauma there's always room for hope, for joy, to reconnect to a world where you feel a part again.

'Seahorses' by Gingerberry Rose

Jim's Advice

n o matter what happens, don't panic. There will be time for all emotions in the fulcrum of the mind, whether they spill out into the spheres of others or crash on inner shores of the mind; the tides and the equilibrium are yours to control and dictate.

Courage is drawn from the strangest places, friends, family support and ultimately the self. Dedication can be encouraged and directed, but again it manifests from the self. All these strengths are practised and developed to hone one's ability to at first cope with and then master being in a comfortable understanding of yourself in the world.

After experiencing significant mental trauma there's always room for hope, for joy, to reconnect to a world where you feel a part again. And these words are as a light on that path toward engaging and immersing again.

Time is gradual, realisation instant. In that constant change continues around us, growth in nature, development in technology, and the human race marches on, and in that race we are all drawn or dragged along. Be the drop in the river flowing forward, not the rock against the tide.

To move with that flow a few key processes can help: a written daily routine, exercise at least twice a day for a minimum of ten minutes, seeing people and making positive interactions. Build strong communal relations and practise activities that you feel good about participating in.

That's the general theory of healthiness out the way, onto the special theories:

Depressives

+ Start your day with a strong positive mantra as you physically exercise, rhythmically breathe and think mindfully about grand scenes of natural magnificence: waterfalls, forests, oceans, mountains, etc.
+ Frequently write lists to give structure to your progress and build an evidence base for your achievements.
+ Find a time each day for new things.
+ Look at what your favourite things are, to do, to eat, to spend on. Evaluate what are good and what are bad for you, actively choose the good habits over the bad and each day reduce the occurrence of bad habits.
+ Slowly over the weeks and months you may notice these things happening anyway, progress is a conal spiral pushing forward through time and we all travel at our own pace, but we all travel.

Maniacs

+ Reign it in. You are in a temporary surge of energy that is being spent from your reserves.

Learning that the energy levels can be controlled, and that holding your silence can be the Main Street valuable.

Doctor's Orders

+ Follow the doctor's advice, take the meds. Do question the advice, read up about your condition and effects of the meds, see the framework that your symptoms fall within, but always remember you are a life outside these symptoms and ultimately are growing toward the symptoms being managed and you as a person being the priority rather than some label of a condition that a doctor has to give you in order to help you.
+ Relapse signatures is a cool term for warning signs; it is crucial that you know the signals and situations that are going to lead to episodes. So write down a list of the signs of mental disruption that you noticed in the run up to a breakdown, this will forewarn you to see where the future takes you.

I am happy to be on medication, which I consider an essential precaution; the suffering of the distress is not worth the risks. To be well on medication is very desirable, much better than worrying about 'when will I be well again' and equating that with getting off medication. People take medication for such a huge range of dangerous health conditions; mental health is no different.

'Tiger' by Daniel

Anne's Story

The Episodes

I am a fifty-four, soon to be fifty-five-year-old female and have had four episodes of mental illness. My first two occurred immediately after the births of our two sons, now aged twenty-eight and twenty-four. I had no problems whatsoever before that. It took around nine months to feel back to normal (and off medication) after the first, and just over a year after the second. For the next twenty years, I was not on medication and led a mental distress-free time. Then I had two episodes close to each other (2010 and 2012) coinciding with the onset of the menopause. I have recovered from these episodes too.

I am happy to be on medication, which I consider an essential precaution; the suffering of the distress is not worth the risks. To be well on medication is very desirable, much better than worrying about 'when will I be well again' and equating that with getting off medication. People take medication for such a huge range of dangerous health conditions; mental health is no different.

One cannot 'will' one's brain never to be in trouble again. I understand now I am more at risk than if I had not had these four episodes. It took me time to 'digest' this but it is very important and I'm at peace with it. I had to do this journey myself.

I am lucky I devised a good system to remember to take the medication; I have no side effects from my maintenance medication and the tests (four times a year) I manage fine. Our local NHS hospital provides these. It's important for me to feel I manage this rather than 'suffer it'; it's a huge mental step which makes a big difference. People have to manage their diabetes, for example.

The episodes all took similar patterns. I was highly manic at the onset of all four and deeply depressed following that, the worst being the last one. I remember being very confused after my first birth as people talked about post-natal depression but no one about puerperal psychosis. This was terribly unsettling and it took six weeks of struggling before anyone noticed I was very sick and the baby not thriving. After our second son was born, it was not really any better as I felt myself falling ill, very ghastly!

The 'menopausal episodes' took us totally by surprise; no one had ever mentioned the possibility I could be unwell again. I felt very angry at that, having carefully avoided more pregnancies and 'depriving us' of more (wonderful) children, I felt desperate to understand the cause of all this.

I have, however, come to think that understanding may not be possible at this stage of our knowledge of our complicated brains: neuroscience, hormones and chemicals, stuff for research, really.

The Symptoms

Some people mention how hard it is to explain to someone how one feels, or how you have been, and that's very true. I remember years after my first puerperal episode reading a mum's account of hers and it was almost a carbon copy of mine; some imagery was, of course, personal but the core of the description very similar: it was very interesting! There are more accounts now as people are less concerned about their mental history being known.

The 'highs' are just as ghastly as the 'lows'. In the general culture, I get a sense the 'highs' are associated with drugs and 'pleasure'. However I found the term very misleading as I experienced mine as very frightening, exhausting and very very isolating.

I was interviewed by the Birmingham Bipolar Disorder Research Network between my menopausal episodes (that was tiring!) and they asked about manic symptoms such as 'voices, visions, etc'. I tried to explain they were NOT imaginary but something I felt the brain actually produced, neurons firing or misfiring creating the 'experience'. A comparable image is an amputee still feeling pain in the missing limb, not very easy to understand if you have not got a missing limb nor have ever been psychotic… Explaining, or trying to, is really tricky.

Precursor signs of serious behavioural changes may help one pick things up faster but it's hard to get the balance between monitoring and obsessive over-diligence. Detailed descriptions I fear are painful and scary for loved ones to hear.

Care and acceptance is terribly important. Those able to sit with the pain and distress are most comforting. A problem is that one is not easy to sit with when manic, everyone wants to 'calm you down' when your brain is telling you to do the opposite: not easy.

Walks, nature, physical activities, music all helped me. Medication of course does work, it brings you down from the unhealthy high: very necessary but tough and painful as it may force the brain down a little fast. Going cold turkey for a smoker or an alcoholic may be an analogy, although I have no experience of that! Being kept safe is part of the picture and that's important to remember.

Being low at the other end is no better! The low 'filter' is terrible too. To the outside world you are less of 'a problem', less goes on the outside, but in the head things unravel literally to a dead end. It is as if the neurons, having worked themselves in a twisted, frantic state, untangle to a flat, lifeless mesh, nothing left! I am writing this now, but at the time it's not a 'writing' or a 'concept', it's something I physically felt each time. Again someone able just to sit with that, not trying to fix me, I found very comforting.

It's an equally dangerous time if not more so. Those who have had the misfortune of facing the wall of no perceived hope can understand why some decide to end their lives. I glimpsed that space on my last episode.

Being able to say how scary that is in the safe environment of my husband's constant, total and unconditional love as well as the power of life itself meant I did not stay there long, recovered slowly and am again leading a normal, rounded life with its normal ups and downs.

Consciousness

I felt very fortunate during each of my bad times that I retained some awareness/consciousness of what was going on beyond how I was feeling/behaving and what was administered to me.

I think it helped as it showed me a piece of my being was still there. I know that was the case as I am able to recall precise events or comments (however bizarre or disturbing) of which relatives or carers thought I was oblivious.

It has made me quite careful not to make assumptions about other people's awareness, whatever the circumstances they find themselves in or the behaviour they display. My memory of specifics is clear, not that I particularly wish to recall them!

Care Environments

My first post-natal episode was managed at home by an excellent GP and a stream of helpful relatives and nannies with a very clear and able NHS consultant in the background. This may sound really good, but actually it was tough. I found it hard to be really unwell in my home; it became a 'sick place'. I was lucky we moved abroad with my husband's work just after our first son turned one.

As a young mum you really miss out, not only on the early bond and months of your baby but on all the networks available to meet other mums. But normality, work and the joy of a delightful toddler followed, and we decided to enlarge our family with a second child. We were told it was very unlikely I would be unwell again…

We returned to London to be seen if necessary by my original consultant. No pre-birth treatment or even assessment was on the map in those days. This was pre-internet time and little did we know the consultant had moved; we could not trace her and no one seemed to know where to guide us.

For this second birth, there was the added pressure of the first child to look after and it was decided to admit me to a private hospital which had a mother and baby unit. We had private insurance by then, and that was covered. We subsequently discovered it stopped covering for mental health immediately after my episode...

There is no time at all to reflect and act in the face of psychotic symptoms; they are in front of you before you know it! You do the best you can, family was again essential. Just as things start very quickly, the timescale of recovery is terribly long and I think this is a real care issue problem there too.

This was the worst of my care in many ways: mostly the incompetence of the hospital consultant, who refused to prescribe what had worked for me before, and (with some few exceptions: art therapist and some lovely nurses) the staff were hostile and used to depressive mothers not manic ones. My menopausal episodes took me first to a local NHS A&E department where I felt myself getting worse as no one had the slightest idea how to look after me there. It may sound melodramatic but it was like being in a cage and you would think of releasing or putting down an animal if it displayed that level of suffering...

Later, my GP recommended a consultant (who worked both privately and in the NHS) and admission to a fairly local clinic. We paid ourselves for the whole thing. Not everyone can do that! The staff were pretty good, there was a small outdoor space – enough not to feel totally in prison – the consultant did his best with medication, was very experienced, clear-headed, as well as a very 'human person'! The experience of the illness was just as bad, but a decent environment did not apply extra layers of difficulties and the medical care was as good as I could get.

I later had the help of an excellent therapist for a short but very useful course of cognitive therapy through the NHS. I requested this via my GP. One needs energy to do that; you need to be well and assertive to help yourself. It is truly sad how mental health remains the poorer cousin of physical health. Access to decent healthcare, whether it's a cardiologist, a wheelchair or a good psychiatrist consultant, should not be so different!

Telling One's Story

I am not sure I resonate with that! I'm happy to share the experience, as this writing testifies. I have always been open about my mental history but do not feel the need to dwell on it either. My mental health is not 'a story', it's part of my life; it's me as much as my brown eyes, my personality, my upbringing and my ancestors' gene pool, no less but no more. It's never mundane nor anecdotal, and always quite tiring to churn over. Love, good medical care, work (I am lucky I love my work and returning to it one of the best things for me!), singing, physical activities all good.

I did a mindfulness course recently; this was a good extension for me of years of various helpful meditative practices and it helps me make sure I take the breaks I need to look after myself. I do not know if and when something might rock the boat badly again, but I am well enough again to feel I do not want to be constantly hostage to the possibility it might.

From the hospital I was luckily referred to a therapeutic community... After a year there I left and took up a place at a teacher training college. After leaving there I trained as an actor. After working for years I trained as a voice teacher. I now teach actors as well as working as one.

'Seahorses 2' by Gingerberry Rose

Andrew's Story

When I was seventeen, living in South Africa, my father committed suicide. He had been depressed and had a bad case of shingles, but apart from that, no one knows quite why he did it. My response was to be strong for my mother and not let it affect me at all. I determinedly sat my school-leaving exams a week later and got through (apart from a maths re-sit).

I took a job for a few months before deciding I wanted to see the world. With my mother's blessing I worked a passage from Cape Town to Liverpool and hitchhiked through Belgium, Holland, Norway and Sweden. Returning to South Africa, I went to university, graduated and got a job in advertising. All this time I had not looked at my feelings about my father's death. I hadn't grieved at all.

I got bored with advertising and decided to go to England. I took a one-way ticket and with no planning turned up on the doorstep of a friend in London. I got a menial job in London and then after a few months moved to Exeter where another friend was living. After working there for a while I moved back to London where I shared a house with some fellow expats. It was there, working nights at a theatre and feeling terribly isolated, that I became depressed. My mother, on a visit, became concerned and offered to fly me home to South Africa for a rest.

That felt like it would have been a defeat, so I declined. I became more depressed and finally swallowed the best part of a bottle of paracetamol. Luckily one of my flatmates found me and got me to casualty where I had my stomach pumped. As I groggily came round I had a bizarre experience. At the foot of my bed was a junior doctor who had been a prefect at my private school in South Africa. He proceeded to lecture me on what a disgrace I was, with all the advantages I'd had in life, to attempt suicide.

From the hospital I was luckily referred to a therapeutic community where talking therapy was all that was offered. After a year there I left and took up a place at a teacher training college. After leaving there I trained as an actor. After working for years I trained as a voice teacher. I now teach actors as well as working as one.

I must thank the NHS services for the services they have provided for me because I know deep down they have probably saved my life.

'Tree' by Charlotte

John B's Story

If I am honest with myself I think I knew but chose to ignore the signs, perhaps because of my fear of the stigma and of how people may change their attitudes towards me or by then I was beyond caring.

My depression is perhaps many-faceted but what has certainly drained my capacity to keep positive has been the fact that I have been subjected to bullying for the past decade. Like all bullying it has had peaks and troughs, but it has been eating away at me and one day in February I just had nothing left. I guess some will wonder how I can be experiencing bullying, but if there is one thing that I have learnt from representing members, it is that anyone can be bullied. I have learnt as a social worker and trade union rep bullying can happen to all of us. Often bullying takes place and other work colleagues know it is taking place but don't say anything for fear that the bullying will move to them. I do understand why others have stayed silent and I don't blame them, but we all have our limits.

A good friend who shared their experience of depression best summed it up by saying, "You are completely drained like a car battery; you can't drive with a dead battery." This resonated with me as I just woke up one day and something had happened. My colleagues in the UNISON office all said that they were not surprised, as they were only wondering when it would happen.

It did take a lot of persuading to see my GP; my workload is always crazy and I do admit I take the attacks on my members personally. I am always thinking about what we are doing, how we can improve and what we do next. I am based in a council which six years ago announced it was going for mass outsourcing, though they deny it; at least twenty-two council services have now been outsourced to another employer in the last four years and the last of us are now due to be outsourced by April next year. The stress and anxiety being experienced by our members is intolerable and therefore I am always trying to find different ways to support them.

On the day I decided to visit my GP, I can't pretend it wasn't very stressful because I feared just what he might say; I genuinely wondered if I was going to be sectioned as I knew I was in a bad way.

I am glad I saw my GP and whilst I was not keen on taking medication I recognised I had taken the first step by finally acknowledging I had a serious problem. I could no longer pretend it wasn't there. By the second visit to the GP I agreed a treatment plan with counselling and, reluctantly, medication.

Now after several months of treatment, I am glad to report that I am starting to feel better. I am still struggling with the side effects of the medication which sometimes impacts on the quality of my life. As someone who has never taken medication, this is still an area I am struggling with.

I must thank the NHS services for the services they have provided for me because I know deep down they have probably saved my life. Just writing those words, 'saved my life', is still quite sobering and there are times when I can't believe how I got into such a state.

Since my condition has become known to some of my friends, some of them have shared their own experiences of depression. It is no surprise to me that each of us has a different experience of how it impacts our mental health. As a practitioner in mental health and now a service user, I recognise much more the importance of seeking help. Sometimes first contact might not be a positive experience but don't give up because the NHS hopefully won't give up on you. I know that mental health services are being decimated and there is an increased need for services, which is why we must all actively campaign to stop the destruction of mental health services.

Many friends and comrades have wondered where I had gone and for those sending messages of support a big thanks, you don't realise just how much messages do help. I have started going back to work gradually, I've had a few relapses as I have tried to take too much on, so I am going to try and slow down… honest!

"Depression is the most unpleasant thing I have ever experienced… It is that absence of being able to envisage that you will ever be cheerful again. The absence of hope. That very deadened feeling, which is so very different from feeling sad. Sad hurts but it's a healthy feeling. It is a necessary thing to feel. Depression is very different."[1]

– J.K. Rowling

1. www.howibeatdepression.com/how-jk-rowling-beat-depression

Some of you may have seen my post 'Living with Depression' which I shared on Facebook after a long absence from work.

http://johnburgess001.blogspot.co.uk/2016/08/
living-with-depression.html

I am now at the end of my phased return to work. I am full-time as from tomorrow, but I want to share some of the feedback I have received – most of it positive and one a bit sinister.

My first worry was judging how much to say as I had been away for a long time. I have to admit I was worried about the stigma and the way people would treat me. By that I meant: would people lose confidence in me? Would people avoid speaking to me because they weren't sure I was mentally strong enough to help them? I also had a nagging feeling that I am not sure how right I am, if that means anything? In the end I decided I would just come out and say: "I've had a breakdown," and it hasn't been too bad. I have had lots of positive feedback from members, wishing me well and several have divulged their own mental health problems and all of them have been surprised that I have been struggling with depression. But that is the problem with mental health: it is not something most of us feel comfortable with, it's invisible, which is why so many of us (me included) are able to cover it up.

I have been a worker in mental health services for more than twenty years and yet it does feel nothing much has changed. People are still struggling to feel confident to disclose to their families, friends and employer for fear of the consequences. There is so much more work that needs to be done to address stigma and mental health, which is why I wasn't happy when Owen Smith at first denied he called Jeremy Corbyn 'a lunatic'. My anger was because he tried to deny it until the video appeared. In terms of my employment I want to be clear that my employer has been very supportive and as someone who has also represented workers with mental health problems I would expect every worker to be given the same level of support and understanding.

There is an irony that has not been lost on me. Before my breakdown I was for four years negotiating pay and grading proposals. One of the proposals was to drastically cut our local government sick pay scheme. The council reflected on our arguments and dropped this proposal. If UNISON had not been organised in our council, this proposal would have gone through and I would have been sacked. I know from experience with the private sector organisations I now have to deal with that someone in similar circumstances would highly likely be sacked. The rapid erosion of hard-won terms and conditions is being accelerated by privatisation and is one of many reasons why our branch works so hard to oppose outsourcing.

I am now taking medication along with counselling. For anyone who has worked with me in mental health services, taking medication was a major trauma for me. Now I am learning to live with the same side effects I have seen impacting on other mental health service users and, of course, my mother, who has for the last seven years been living with dementia, with teeth grinding, hot flushes, cramps, tiredness, yawning, biting of the tongue.

Work colleagues and members have all shared their own experiences of taking mental health medication. Only today I had a conversation with someone who very much needs help but is so worried about side effects of medication. All I can say, it is *different for everyone*, and if you do have to take medication it is really important you take notes of any side effects and visit your GP. Having said all that I do want to come off the medication, but I am concerned about what will happen if I do, could I face going through what has been hell again? That in itself causes me anxiety, to think that I am not sure if I am okay, is the medication working, have I got better and what happens if I come off it and relapse?

But I recognise I have been lucky in that I have been able to access counselling through my GP surgery. Many people I have spoken to since I went public have said they have not had this as an option because of the lengthy waiting lists. I was lucky because my GP surgery had its own counsellors and so I have had free access to counselling. I am very clear that without this support I am not sure I would be at work now. But when I was working in mental health services, this option was hardly ever an option because of the length of the waiting lists. Hence why medication which should complement treatment was often the only treatment for people using mental health services.

And now…The brutal austerity attacks on all public services, but in particular mental health services are another reason why I passionately supported Jeremy Corbyn and his team. It is ridiculous to talk about supporting people with mental health issues to get them back into work if you don't have *free access to counselling* to complement other treatments.

I would like to highlight one of Jeremy's 2017 ten pledges was 'Secure Our NHS and Social Care', which stated:

"We will end health service privatisation and bring services into a secure, publicly provided NHS. We will integrate the NHS and social care for older and disabled people, funding dignity across the board and ensure parity for mental health services."

This still sounds good to me.

Recently news broke about funding cuts coming to the NHS; today a story broke of surgery being rationed. In my view we can't let this happen, we must stand up and fight for our NHS. After all, if they were able to create the NHS after the Second World War, then a country which is often touted as the fifth or sixth richest country in the world can surely *invest and secure* our wonderful NHS for future generations to come.

This is why I tried to find the energy to do all I could to help Jeremy in the general election.

Lastly but most importantly I can't write this post without mentioning news of a group of inspirational/heroic anti-austerity campaigners, the 'Disabled People Against Cuts (DPAC)'.

In the Barnet UNISON office the fight for our members seems bigger than ever, so much change and so much work to do and so much energy needed to help everyone. I am absolutely *100%* proud to belong to our branch and to have the honour to work with the office staff, branch officers, local reps, all of whom are doing all that they can to support our members and defend public services.

Solidarity,
John

People with mental health problems are often not easy to be around, but we are still human like everyone else, have the same needs, hopes, desires. We are just different, that's all.

'Wheel' by Charlotte

Sophie's Story

Schizophrenia is known and understood as a young person's illness (which doesn't mean you cannot get it when you are older) but most people who are diagnosed with it are in their teens and early twenties. (I was diagnosed at twenty-five; the therapists who were seeing me at the time suggested that I had in fact been carrying it for a long time, but being a strong character I had managed somehow to carry it.)

It's about, or was in my case about always trying to find the meaning in and about everything. When I attended a support group for people with schizophrenia we all had our lengthy, epic stories of exploration into unknown and unanswered riddles and questions. Mine concerned where we come from, the universe and stuff. It was over twenty years ago now so I am struggling to remember, but I recall having very vivid dreams about aliens and then spending the next day or week or so trying to work out what this all meant.

So these are the type of brain activity going on in the mind of someone who has or is developing schizophrenia. Mostly we wouldn't be openly discussing these things because we might have tried but been ridiculed. At the same time, though, our interpersonal relationships may either be deteriorating or already highly antagonistic/problematic, causing more and more isolation.

Then there are florid symptoms, such as hallucinations – visual, auditory, tactile; you can even smell things that aren't there too. The voices I heard were initially comforting me and then, after a while, became malevolent.

I had the feeling of being directly referred to and talked about in the media, on the radio and on the TV. This was excruciatingly painful and as I felt I was a character being analysed and/or assassinated, I almost became catatonic as I listened and imagined being talked to and about by people on TV and on the radio.

All of this happens simultaneously; there is no chronology, but the symptoms get worse and crescendo. At the peak of it for me I would have most likely died but for one of my neighbours who phoned the police because I ran out into the middle of the road screaming one night. (I was actually looking for someone from the radio who I believed was in close proximity to where I was living.) So I was taken in by the police and from there went to a psychiatric hospital. It did save my life, although the amount of meds I was put on almost killed me but that is the subject for the next instalment.

Schizophrenia – Worst. Illness. Ever.

So now I found myself in a psychiatric hospital, where the staff were kind on the whole but I was sure they were making a mistake by incarcerating me and that it would all come out soon that I was not meant to be there. Meanwhile I was taking the medication, although at first I refused and refused again… The medication was strong: chlorpromazine; it made all my muscles seize up and I could hardly walk and had strange, twisted-up movements. I was also put on haloperidol, which is considered an anti-violent drug, then depixol injection, once I was in agreement with a drug regime.

I was on so much medication that at one point I could barely walk. Then I was advised by cognitive behavioural therapists who were seeing me to only agree to the injection. I saw so much while I was there, from people being forcibly injected on the floor in front of everyone to the instance of a really nice middle-aged lady coming in suffering from depression who was prescribed Electroconvulsive Therapy, and after a few sessions she went mute; it was terrible. And all sorts of other things. I felt sorry for some of the staff too, especially the ones who didn't have a clue what they were doing. One nurse who thought she was being proactive with us and was really good ended up with someone throwing a knife at her… The cleaning staff and students were much more available to us than the qualified staff.

There was a super occupational therapy department where you could play badminton, muck about with those huge gym balls, do cookery, painting, and drawing. They also kept animals – rabbits and guinea pigs. Another OT department at the same place on a different site had a music studio, a place to do pottery and woodwork. Those places were great; I knew it was good but I was having such a bad time myself it was hard to enjoy it, although it was top-quality therapy.

The hospital was an old converted workhouse, and there were a lot of conversations taking place: while I was there they made a very nice female-only ward, which was the last ward I was on. I requested to be placed there as I didn't want the hassle of dealing with the opposite sex while I was so ill. This ward was really nice and I was finally starting to feel better. They spent a lot of money on it, then three months later (after I had been discharged) they demolished it. I was absolutely gutted and incensed. Looking back, that was just the first stage of the wholesale destruction of psychiatric services that has taken place, and a lot of it in the name of 'recovery'! It would be ironic if it wasn't so tragic.

If I had been born twenty years later, I am sure that because of the severity of symptoms I experienced I would have died because they hardly give you any help these days; the hospitals are strict regimes now where the emphasis is on 'sight lines'. I could go on, and I will in the next instalment.

Living with Schizophrenia - Disability

To just be starting out in life and have it knocked down so drastically whereby you are rendered disabled is an unimaginable blow. It was so hard to accept that there is no cure, that you are changed and have limitations, that you have to have less expectations from life; I could barely accept it and believed (falsely) and for quite a while that I had had a nervous breakdown but I would and could still get myself up and 'recover'. The recovery model did in fact start from this type of attitude being voiced by service users like myself from that time.

It was a concern of mine that although I appeared the same as I always did (basically – minus some stiffness and perhaps the odd shifty look that had not been there previously) I had changed so much. I felt like the old me had died; I no longer existed as I had. I was concerned that people who knew the old me would not understand this death I was and had experienced. It was particularly hard and disorientating for my family. I did not wish to return to my hometown at that time as I did not want people who knew me to see me like that. It was vain I guess, but that was how I felt.

More than anything I wanted to fit in with life and this was something that was impossible. It was an impossible situation; I was and became more and more withdrawn. I was suicidal for a long time. I wanted to die almost every day and it went on for many years too. Schizophrenia really is the worst illness ever.

Simultaneous to this severe and underlying or reactive (as the professionals called it) depression, I was trying to figure out how to move on and go forward. One conclusion I came to was that due to the astonishing emptiness and void I was feeling in myself, I would not survive unless I could feel love, that life would not last long, and I was a survivor.

Although it was impossible to love myself at that time, I was able to and felt it necessary to love others. This was about survival; I learned to love others unconditionally. It was not through altruism, it was to survive.

It worked, and became a strong asset in my life. I noticed how I was able to 'heal' people in their spirit and later on I found that this had developed to such an extent that I had learned a form of reiki healing whereby I was able to heal broken bones, tendons and other ailments.

So there it is, out of the fire and all that. I did still carry an immense negativity that I had to deal with. That will be the subject of the next instalment.

Schizophrenia and Schizophrenia...

As you probably know there are different types of schizophrenia, professionals in the field might use a variation of categories, paranoid schizophrenia is one that springs to mind. For service users, a diagnosis might indicate some things but the reality of living with any mental condition is that the lines of categorisation can be thin, blurry, maybe even non-existent.

In my experience, though, looking back on it, the label can outcast a person – drastically, and within those who are diagnosed with schizophrenia, there is a category of people who find themselves together with others, not through the design of psychiatric services but through something else. Basically there are those who have had and maybe still do have the florid symptoms of schizophrenia such as hearing voices, etc., together with severe flatness and negativity, and then, on top of that, there are those who have had and maybe still do have encounters with the devil. I am in that category, and that is/was a very severe situation. One of the most necessary ways of dealing with it was to be able to discuss this with other people who also encounter/ed him, other service users. It had to be in a trusting and amenable environment too. Nobody can bring out a conversation about this other than the person themselves; due to the nature of it, most people who have/had encounters like this will feel highly suspicious of others but have great needs to discuss it with fellows.

So this was my situation, and I did always find others similar to me, although we were a small minority of the people with a diagnosis of schizophrenia. We would talk primarily about what happened and how we reacted to it, and in every case it was different. The funniest example of how one of my friends reacted to seeing and encountering the devil was that my friend smiled! He showed no fear, his explanation of this was that if the devil existed, so too did God, which he was pleased about to know. (I thought that pretty clever of him myself.) I initially saw the devil appear through one of my speakers of my stereo system and I reacted by trying to punch him (lol) – but hurt my hand on the metal and wood of the speaker.

No amount of medication will eradicate your experience, as it is part of you. I discovered that there were many people who had a diagnosis of schizophrenia who had become evangelically religious as a result. As you can imagine that was the last thing I wished to happen given that I had always been atheist and from an atheist family. But that negativity in spirit would not leave me, so after a trip to India in 1999 where I had religious experiences, I was on a road in life that involved a belief system.

It was hard given the circles I frequented; there were socialists and they often assumed hostility towards religious people. I read a lot of classical Marxist literature on the subject of religion and felt that from the classics, there was no hostility. I did not want to be outcast from my socialist friends I had made and be forced into establishment religion, and so I did argue with socialists concerning their assumed atheism, as some of my friends and comrades might recall.

So, that's it. I am still here despite the slings and arrows of outrageous fortune. Amazing that I made it this far and I am grateful for all, for everyone who has been there for me, it was and is still a thankless task. People with mental health problems are often not easy to be around, but we are still human like everyone else, have the same needs, hopes, desires. We are just different, that's all.

I try to create an environment where my life is steady. Regular sleep, careful monitoring of my lifestyle and exercise.

'Which way birds?' by Daniel

Interview with Sheila

Q. *When did you first notice that you felt challenged by your mental health condition?*
A. When I was eighteen years old, thirty-four years ago.

Q. *What happened?*
A. I can't remember the exact details of how my mood became elevated.

Q. *What do you think triggered this distress?*
A. In the immediate, I had taken LSD for the first and only time and I think this must have switched on the capacity I have for bipolar episodes. Past events in my life contribute as well, such as the death of my father when I was ten and the suicide of my grandmother the following year.

Q. *How did your distress progress?*
A. In the early years I managed not to have a full-blown episode for seven years, although

I suffered from months of depression, times when I was unmotivated and unable to function day to day.

Q. *When was the worst time?*
A. In recent years manic episodes and hospital admissions have become more frequent, every twelve to eighteen months, and this has interfered with my work and personal life.

Q. *How did you get through this? What techniques did you use to deal with your distress?*
A. I try to create an environment where my life is steady. Regular sleep, careful monitoring of my lifestyle and exercise. For many years I saw a psychiatrist or psychoanalyst. Getting through the episodes themselves is difficult, but I am lucky in that they generally pass quickly, within a month, and the further recovery period is quick. Sometimes I have kept a mood diary.

Q. *How did people come to your aid? What helped?*
A. I have friends and family who try to help when I show signs of becoming ill. Sometimes it is not caught in time and then I am reluctant to accept I am becoming ill. I had a particular psychiatrist, Dr Massimo Riccio of the Priory, whom I saw weekly and during my thirties, with his help, I managed not to have an episode for five years.

Q. *What was not so helpful?*
A. There is very little outpatient support from the NHS. In the first stage after an admission a

psychiatrist sees you a few times but then the system signs you off and this is really when I would need the support. The appointments are very short, ten minutes or so, and the doctor is not someone you already know and have a relationship with, so it is near impossible for them and you to build a situation where the signs are spotted and a further episode is avoided.

Q. *How were you treated by your local mental health services?*

A. I have had so many admissions in so many different institutions that this is difficult to answer. Over the last ten years many units have closed down. Staff change more frequently, so if you do have frequent admissions you usually go back to a different ward with new faces. Nurses seem to have less and less time and less and less training in the specifics of mental health. As you only ever see your consultant in a ward round, to assess your progress, you are not receiving any therapeutic input.

Many years ago when I went to the Maudsley they provided a psychiatrist for hour-long sessions as part of the treatment. I have experienced private care. The staffing levels are the same, the cost to the patient is the same as the NHS are spending on the patient and yet the nursing staff interact with you and you receive therapy from your psychiatrist. This makes me think that it must be possible to achieve a better level of comfort and patient/doctor and nurse interaction in the local mental health services. Currently local health services for inpatients provide a seedy environment, where violent patients are put alongside vulnerable people; there is nothing to do, which adds to the anxiety, and the environment is dirty and unpleasant. The food is unhealthy.

The art therapy and such is only available to a few and usually doesn't kick in until you are just about to be discharged. The treatment overall is doled out on a hit and miss basis. Notes from prior admissions and outpatient doctors never seem to arrive or if they do they are more than often not consulted. So with no therapy, nurses who have little time, inclination, intelligence and training, the hospital experience is one where the patient is simply herded around, with little space to relax, treated in an ad hoc way in the hope that they will show some basic signs which allow them to be discharged.

Q. *What was your experience with different medications?*

A. I have been taking lithium since my mid-twenties, when I was admitted to the Priory and they diagnosed me as bipolar. This diagnosis had not been reached on my first admittance when I was eighteen to the Maudsley and I had not been medicated in the interim.

Sometimes I have taken a break from the lithium and taken Depakote. Now I take both as the psychiatrist thinks it may help to reduce the frequency of my episodes in recent years. I think for my condition lithium is an excellent solution, however in itself it does not always prevent the illness. Therapeutic intervention and self-knowledge are also necessary. The anti-psychotics that are dispensed to treat one when in an acute episode are not easy to deal with. I find the side effects are excessive and immediate, weight-gain, tremors, etc.

Q. *How are you feeling nowadays?*
A. Currently I am well and balanced, but I did have a very difficult admission last year and the experience in itself was something to recover from.

Q. *Do you have any advice for people suffering from similar mental health challenges?*
   How should families and friends help?
A. Each case and each distress is so different this is difficult to answer. Try to encourage the sufferer to stay out of hospital and if an admission is necessary make sure that they are visited often, perhaps with food, things to remind them of home, enough clothes, etc. If it is affordable, organise some sort of therapist for them on a regular basis. Any sort of mindfulness, yoga, meditation, helps to balance one's moods.

On a sunny autumnal day late in 2003, Anne, an older cousin who had herself experienced post-natal depression, told me something particularly helpful at that time, which was: it won't last forever. For the previous few months I couldn't see a way out - I assumed that my deep sadness would go on indefinitely. But she gave me hope.

'Zebra' by Daniel

Harry's Story

Episode 1

In the summer of 2003 my world was turned upside down. I was twenty, an outgoing university student with a full life – a year into an engaging philosophy degree, a keen campaigner, the heart and soul of the party, with a loving girlfriend and a large circle of friends. Then, while on vacation from university, living at home and attending a week-long political conference in London, my mind started racing. I became obsessive, compulsive and over-confident, often making contributions to discussions I knew little about. These symptoms had been mounting for some time without me noticing but at the conference they accelerated. Then one evening, just when I was feeling like I needed to go home and get some rest, I decided to attend a counter-demonstration against a nearby fascist march, after which I became paranoid and unable to turn off my mind, and stopped sleeping at night. I soon became convinced by a delusional insight – that sleep was a con and that I only needed rest and not necessarily sleep.

This led to a downward spiral. I spent whole nights awake. Soon my daytime became like nightmares as my brain, running wild and wired from lack of sleep, would not slow down.

Following the conference my mental distress escalated. I visited a friend who told me I appeared to be stuck in 'argument mode'. At home I started thinking that I was being spied on by the secret service using spyware operating through the smoke alarms. I smashed the smoke alarms with a hammer. This was when my family knew there was something wrong. I was now stuck in a fixed state of delusion and paranoia. I didn't know that there was anything wrong with me but those around me – my family and friends – were confounded. What was going on?

I was having a nervous breakdown, my first episode of psychosis. I was *fearful* and could not think properly – I found it difficult to rationalise or reason. Instead I would see added significance in the smallest innocent gesture. When lunching at a local pub I saw a dessert listed as 'Death by Chocolate', which I took literally and thought I'd call 'their' bluff and order it! At home I thought a Safeways chicken was poisoned and ate it anyway. I felt unable to resist the pull of paranoid delusions. I became delerious with making mental connections internally and externally (what the Germans call *Beziehungswahn*) and believed that to be life's purpose. And I couldn't sleep.

When my mum realised that I was mentally disturbed she phoned the GP, who recommended that the local Crisis Team should assess my case. The Crisis Team consisted of eighteen NHS staff – social workers, psychiatric nurses, and led by a psychiatrist. After an inital psychological assessment they regularly visited with different individuals at each twice-daily visit. Some of them helped and some made me anxious. The psychiatrist prescribed me with sleeping tablets to help me sleep and risperidone, an anti-psychotic sedative, which slowly reduced my symptoms of psychosis but also seemed to numb my brain.

Initially I was full of doubts. Why, I wondered, were the medication container tubs the Crisis Team gave me in various colours? (The colours were in fact arbitrary.) Why did some of the team wear thick reflective sunglasses which prevented eye contact? (I also felt insecure about their jewellery for some reason.) Why did some of them not wear identity cards to confirm their role? Why were the ID cards in different formats? Why were my blood and urine test results lost? (I never did find out the results, which would at least have shown the evidence of the hash cakes I had recently eaten, or the crack I think I may have once recently smoked.) I remember it being a very confusing time, like something from a scary novel or film. Being presented with the Crisis Team's varying personalities and contradictory advice was perplexing.

The subject of my paranoid thoughts was political. My fears about being spied upon by the state combined with other delusions, visual and auditory, fuelling my acute anxiety. I thought that some of the activists I had been talking to at the conference were spies and that they had spiked my drinks. I thought that the builders next door were being noisy on purpose – to disturb me mentally.

And the national political context seemed to reinforce such fears. My mother tried to hide alarmist newspapers from me, but I saw some unsettling stories, such as government scientist Dr David Kelly dying in mysterious circumstances. The country seemed a scary and confusing place. I thought that everyone I met had motives for or against me, that they were polarised as either good or evil, and often evil. Even strangers asking directions in the street seemed to have another agenda. I thought messages were being broadcast to or about me on the TV and radio.

Looking back I can see how self-orientated my mental distress was, how central I thought I was to everything. At the time my mum told me that I was 'small fry', that strangers were not really interested in me. She, my dad and my older brother tried to convince me that I need not worry, but I was stuck in fear of almost everyone and everything. My brother once asked me to identify which bathroom products I was paranoid about and I identified being fearful about most of them.

The paranoid psychosis that I was locked into was frightening. When paranoid, I found it difficult to differentiate between reality and fantasy. I could not filter out irrational thoughts, establish clarity, or determine logic or truth. One paranoid fantasy was that there was a cavern of spies under the patio, another that there were poisonous venomous snakes in the garden, another that there was a bomb planted under my piano. So I avoided practising the piano. I thought my family and I were at risk – that we would be shot and that I had to protect them. I saw things move within the curtains, saw non-existent faces, and heard voices that seemed to come from within and without of myself. I once went 'on walkabout', wandering around North London, walking into strangers' houses looking for my girlfriend, asking an old man for some fruit (which he gave me)!

Although I was formally diagnosed as suffering from a 'first episode of psychosis', being trapped in the condition, I couldn't make sense of the label. My mum told me I was having a 'nervous breakdown', which made some sense to me but did not prevent my symptoms of paranoia, unrealistic suspicions about other people and their motives, and delusions and anxiety about being personally persecuted. I remained trapped in fear, overwhelmed by fantasies and delusions for two months. I did have some moments of sanity or 'insight', as one mental health worker put it, which helped see me through the nightmare, but these were mainly dark days.

As I was exhausting and distressing my mother and brother at home, after six weeks I was advised to take up the offer of a room at a nearby respite hostel, a 'halfway' house, which I accepted. It was a diverse, friendly place with service users mixed in age, gender and background, supporting people in a range of conditions. I found it comforting, given my mental condition. The house was a large, spacious Victorian building on a busy city road but opposite a park with a cafe. I shared its accommodation and facilities with a gambling addict, an alcoholic, people with depression, and others with psychosis. My bedroom was spacious with a comfy bed, a sink and a mirror, a clothes cupboard, with a shared bathroom off the hallway. I had a little cupboard in which I put sweets that I got from a pleasant newsagents nearby. Having become quite child-like, I focused my time at the 'Haven' (as it was known) on re-growing emotionally, rationally and in responsibility, to get back to where I was before I got ill. I soon re-established my ability to cook, wash clothes, socialise, and go outside.

Unfortunately the staff who worked there were often undertrained and/or under-nice! Some were manipulative. One staff member seemed to tell me with her eyes to spit out the medication once I was in my room; others tried to get me to change my recorded accounts of staff and service users! And their counselling or 'talk therapy' was not informed nor knowledgeable of any particular approach or of the needs of psychotic patients. Nonetheless, the halfway house provided a space in which I could restart healthy habits and develop a little trust in the world, in a safe, secure and supportive environment, where my family and friends could regularly come to see me.

By September most of the psychosis had gone (it started in July) but I was now faced with a new problem: symptoms of *depression*, a new reality to me as a gregarious, optimistic young man. The symptoms of psychosis such as paranoia and my inability to develop trust and rationalise my thoughts had largely gone but they were replaced with emotional numbness and incapacity to feel joy. Recently I found a word for some of what I experienced: 'anhedonia', which involves reduced motivation and inability to experience pleasure or 'hedonic functioning'. Everyday tasks became such a hassle. I didn't shave my beard for three months! I felt like I had cotton wool in my head, that my brain wasn't working properly. When I ate out I could not be upright and instead had to lie down on restaurant booths; at department stores I had to lie on the beds. I deferred my next year at uni to the following year and attempted a couple of history modules at a local college in London but did not have the mental capacity to complete them.

The fearful high I experienced in the summer of 2003 and the low that replaced it during the following winter took its toll on my brother, father and my mother, who was my primary carer. My mum was very supportive. She dedicated time and energy into my recovery and coped brilliantly. She got involved in local carer's groups and health campaigns (which later culminated in saving the local hospital's accident and emergency department from closure, as well as later saving the hospital itself). My brother and dad also did all they could. Collectively, my strong family was central to my recoveries, and their support was fundamental in helping me dig myself out of deep troughs of fear and despair.

When the Crisis Team judged me to be no longer 'in crisis' they stopped visiting me, although it was months before the Early Intervention for Psychosis Team allocated me a key worker, a Community Psychiatric Nurse (CPN). But she was not very helpful. I saw her for two and a half years, with little progress. She kept going over what had triggered my distress originally. She focused on the impact of 'distractions' that centred me and fleetingly snapped me out of depression like playing the Who's Who? boardgame. But at the time I thought that I was more useful to her research than she was to my mental wellbeing! She had no ambition for *my* ambition to get back to the person I once was.

Around this time my dad showed me a newspaper article about how musician Sheryl Crow combated depression through exercise. I received a 'prescription for exercise' from my local council, but as it was limited to early mornings and busy lunch hours I was often – ironically – too lethargic or socially anxious to make use of it. My friend's dad took me cycling to a local swimming pool during that very cold autumn but as my medication caused lethargy and he liked to swim at 8am, I found this difficult to achieve. Still, it felt good to swim.

Clinical depression left me flat, demotivated and very sad. The distress it caused forced me to defer my university studies; my girlfriend could not cope with my distress and split up with me. The medication that I took made me depressed and overweight. When under their spell, horrible low moods may appear to have no ending. My CPN said that my depression would follow my psychosis, as night follows day. So when it came, I accepted depression as an unavoidable experience. But on a sunny autumnal day late in 2003, Anne, an older cousin who had herself experienced post-natal illness, told me something particularly helpful at that time, which was: it won't last forever. For the previous few months I couldn't see a way out – I assumed that my deep sadness would go on indefinitely. But she gave me hope. It was bolstering to know that depression is not always lifelong, and can often be managed, even overcome. For now I convalesced: I watched comedy videos, sang in a choir; I was kind to myself. And the following September my cousin was proved right: I got back on track, returning to uni to continue my second year there, a year on from my deferral.

Episode 2

It's curious how often one learns lessons only with the benefit of hindsight. In 2004 my dad sent me a postcard to my university address with the advice, "Don't mix with the drink and drugs set." Both of my parents talked to me about research about psychosis being triggered by skunk use: my mum sent me an article on the matter. If only I'd listened. By the middle of my second term at my original university, I developed a bad reaction to some cannabis I smoked, which gave rise to another bout of delusions and paranoia. I had been smoking cannabis for some time with a uni social group, and now suffered a second nervous breakdown. My dad came to my student house to take me home to London. I sang Beatles songs with him on the train down and, after a difficult spell at home, then went to the halfway house I had attended in 2003. However, I was not admitted because I did not trust them with prescribing my medication and wanted to self-medicate, which they would not allow.

I was in a really bad way with some symptoms that I had not previously experienced, particularly hearing voices. So I agreed to hospitalisation, sanctioned by my psychiatrist, and thankfully got a hospital bed without being sectioned. My room was modern and clean, similar to my room at university halls, with clothes cupboards, bookshelves, a desk, a chair, a nice bed, an en suite sink and a warm(-ish) shower. The hospital workers were often kind and there were supportive occupational therapy classes – a beneficial yoga group, plus art and walking classes. The food was freshly prepared and tasty. Once I felt safe eating it I put on quite a bit of weight! I wrote over one hundred poems and songs during my time in hospital.

Although the ward was locked (ie. the door from the corridor to the ward was locked) I was, between 3–8pm, able to go out, and often went to a beautiful nearby park with family and friends, which alieveated some of the distress of being ill and living with mentally ill people. Surrounded by others suffering as you are suffering, hospital wards can be challenging places to be when you are ill. But as it was professionally staffed, I felt sufficiently safe. Listening to soothing music on headphones before I went to sleep helped. However, it took longer to recover after this episode of psychosis than in 2003.

After hospitalisation I attended some courses at a London university but struggled with the effort of study and reluctantly quit the course. I simply couldn't think properly. Following this episode of psychosis the risperidone I was taking had ceased to be as effective as it was initially. I was prescribed another anti-psychotic: aripiprazole, which I took in increasing doses as the risperidone dose was decreased. But the combination of a new drug that had no effect and the old drug being reduced proved disastrous, and triggered another relapse. So I was in hospital twice in quick succession.

Episode 3

My third breakdown led to a second hospital admission that was tough-going. I was in a bad way when I went there. I felt very insecure, persecuted: I thought that some patients were plying me with spiked drinks; some of the staff were impatient with me and others, sometimes shouting at service users who were in a bad way; and some seemed to lack sympathy or understanding. I was still on the dreaded aripiprazole, which did not help. The workers there obviously had stressful working conditions and were probably fed up with patients' disturbing behaviour. Most weeks my progress and care was assessed in a care plan assessment meeting, which was attended by my psychiatrist, allocated nurse, a string of other professionals I did not know; sometimes with my family, sometimes not. This was a weird, alienating scenario – one in which I was asked personal questions by people I had not met before.

I was then offered another drug, but I thought that its luminous yellow colouring meant that it had some sort of toxic composition. Eventually my older brother persuaded me to give it a go. It was clozapine, a drug considered the last resort in anti-psychotics, usually administered only after at least two other anti-psychotics have been tried first. It has horrible side effects from weight-gain to over-production of saliva, to sleepiness and fatigue and can cause a shortage of white blood cells, making users vulnerable to infection. It requires monitoring: initially through weekly blood tests and then, after for several months, monthly blood tests. Taking clozapine requires strong organisational skills in getting blood tests and collecting meds on time – an additional challenge for individuals confused by psychosis and medication. Still I feel that I am better with it than without even if it is a sedative, not a cure.

It is surprising that, given that one in a hundred people suffer from psychotic illness, the current medication is so inadequate. The brain is one of the most complicated phenomena in the world, and its proper functioning is essential to human progress and general well-being. And yet the combined brain power of some of the world's most cutting-edge scientists have not yet resolved the problem of our own malfunction. (As an optimist I foresee that forthcoming research may yet lead us to a brighter future...) But whatever the solution is, I think medication is only part of the answer.

After I left the hospital I asked to be provided with a new counsellor and was given a social worker who was much better than my previous CPN. He was a nice guy and helped me have a relatively manageable normal life between 2006 and my next breakdown in 2011 with a life full of work, study and socialising. I gained a diploma in Audio Engineering, had a successful term of study at Oxford Brookes and spent two enjoyable years working in an independent bookshop.

Episode 4

Five years on from Episode 3 I relapsed after getting heavily drunk on Merlot, along with other drinks, when celebrating the end of term at a different university, and Episode 4 was unleashed. Like my wishful thinking about cannabis, I did not realise that alcohol could interfere with the clozapine working. My hospital stay was stressful. As a result of economic cutbacks the management no longer allocated beds by residential area, as they had previously, which meant that all of the service users who were at the beginning of their breakdowns were put together, and at their most fragile. One patient tried to break into my room. (Thankfully the doors had locks.) Again staff seemed hostile and fractious. After my first weekend at home on a trial run, the hospital refused to let me return, despite my serious condition. True to form, my mother, father and I led a 'sit down' at the hospital, hoping to secure me with a bed. It worked, but I no longer wanted to stay. So I went to the halfway house.

The halfway house was calming but not very helpful. Although a comforting, spacious place, there were few staff on hand to offer help or support. When I asked for a support worker to come with me to go to the shops down the road, I was told that no one could spare the time. There was rarely anyone about when I needed support. They all seemed to be busy with something else.

I did, however, have some useful epiphanies at this point. It now became clear to me how consuming cannabis and alcohol had meant that my medication had little effect, and made my symptoms worse, and factored into my breakdowns. So in 2011, after leaving the halfway house, I became teetotal. This was difficult, especially in Britain's drink-soaked social scene. Now I have not touched alcohol for nine years. I often have vivid dreams about drinking alcohol(!), but knowing the damage it can do me, inspires me to stay 'on the wagon'. My parents and older brother were always very anti-drugs whereas I from a young age wanted to experiment. Now I hope to spare them and myself from any more drug-fuelled distress.

Road to recovery

In October 2011 I left London to live in the countryside. Moving away from the stresses and strains of the big smoke for quieter country lanes aided my road to recovery. I did some study with the Open University and, with its emphasis on individual study and few lectures to attend, I flourished. I finally got my BA (in English Literature) and followed this up with a MA (in Music) in a course which unfortunately no longer exists! I found study engrossing and a welcome distraction from anxieties. I joined a choir and became its chairperson and made headway with my mental health challenges, aided by a new counsellor. She used a holistic type of Cognitive Behavioural Therapy as part of a research project and although I found it difficult initially, establishing trust with her proved central to my future progress. With her help and support I furthered my understanding of how my lingering symptoms functioned and how they were not part of the essence of who I am, as well as developing coping strategies and behaviours for dealing with them. I am thankful for her helping me to sort myself out, and further distance myself a little from the nasty, persistent symptoms of psychosis. One of the key strategies was to develop some objectivity about my condition, to see things in perspective, as if from a distance, to understand causes, processes and effects.

*

Over the years I have been challenged by the side effects of my medication, particularly gaining weight. Initially, taking risperidone caused lethargy and horrendous weight gain. So, I briefly tried pill-based weight-loss supplements but they were incompatible with my medication. I tried dieting programmes but found them hard to stick to. Then I discovered an online weight-loss programme and lost seven kilos. It's not much, but it's a start and I now (usually) make healthy food choices; I think that I am heading in the right direction. As I write one current consumer fashion for a healthy brain is pre- and pro-biotics, which may prove to be partially effective treatments for mental health problems. But how proficient these solutions are in mental health terms remains to be seen.

Exercise has proved helpful. Yoga and tai chi are known to be beneficial but I found their impact problematic while I still suffer from symptoms of mental disturbance; in some ways they seem to counter the effects of my medication. But I enjoy basic meditation, gym, walking and occasional running. Exercise videos can be good if I feel tired or anxious or if its cold outside.

Musical engagement has proved beneficial – listening, playing and writing it. When mentally challenged, I particularly enjoy listening to music. John Coltrane is probably my favourite. And when anxious or sad I find playing wind instruments helpful. The sadness of some of the many songs I wrote in hospitals and at the halfway house, and others since, shows how I compose as a form of therapy. Whatever happens with the songs – I'm hoping they sell! – I find the creative process of writing music supportive, transformative and cathartic. Playing music helps distract me from self-orientated thinking and composing channels my energies which might otherwise be locked into cycles of anxiety, or being drained or depressed. I'm on the mend.

Ever since my first breakdown seventeen years ago, I have decided to confront my problems, face my fears. I have attended university courses, singing classes, gym sessions, worked and volunteered. I have been kind to myself when convalescing and channelled my creativity into songwriting. Although I have experienced much pain and distress, over the last sixteen years in particular, these experiences have made me who I am and in some respects I feel stronger for it.

*

A problem for all of us with mental health challenges and for those who try to help us is the inadequacy of the mental health care system. To my knowledge the halfway house I stayed in still provides residential care, but its limited number of beds means that it is only for a tiny minority of those who may benefit from it. More funding for more halfway houses, mental health facilities and staff would be a progressive step for any government seriously endeavouring to tackle the acute need for mental health reform.

Mental health hospitals, as with all environments for people with mental health challenges, should be as pleasant as possible, for the well-being of patients and staff. But they seem to fall far short of what is needed. At the time of writing there are many who would benefit from positive residential specialist care but cannot receive it because there are no spare beds. When a bed is urgently needed an unrecovered patient is booted out before they are ready, as they attempted to do to me. The food I had enjoyed during my first hospitalisation was by my most recent time there no longer prepared on site.

Patients may go into hospitals deeply unhappy/disturbed; but they ought to be securely on the road to recovery by the time they leave. Some friends of mine who ended their own lives in their youth may never have done so if they had been admitted during crisis and looked after until mentally securely grounded, or treated effectively and regularly in the community or supported through the education system. If you break your leg you expect to get immediate treatment in our NHS hospitals. It should be the same if you break your mind.

Mental health hospitals should support the many (often young) individuals by providing them with the help they need to get them back on their feet. But of course one needs to be holistic about this and recognise that there is a need for change, not only within hospital services but also in broader society. This means working towards reducing the conditions that give rise to more mental distress, and so tackling the insidiously destructive nature of contemporary society, and thinking about the direction in which we are all headed. This requires not only confronting the wide-scale underfunding of mental health provision but also breaking with the economic priorities of 'Austerity Britain'. This means building a society where everyone's basic needs are met. The money is there to do it, we just need to apply the political will.

Poetry and Lyrics

A certain number of weeks after,
I had a compulsion to watch
Bambi.

Rosie's Poems

Preface

"My mother died of a cancer in her mouth, spreading to her throat, lungs and further. We had just eight months from initial biopsy to hospice admission and she passed away on the first day of my final semester of my undergraduate degree. I spent many train journeys between Southampton and Exeter in the weeks before and after her death, and wrote many of my feelings during those hours sliding past the southern countryside. These poems are selected from the full series I wrote as a narrative of the month before and the six months after we lost her."

C.

Riddled is the word in my mind
But we do not say it.
The atmosphere on the way away is one from a scene
In a film. That you can feel
And mould
Into the pain that everybody feels but
Does not feel.
The tears can stay behind reading glasses
Eyes half full,
Hearts half numb.
Time half slow.

Later
Sleeping in my tears.

The feeling of watching rain on the hills
In the distance.
Watching a plague fall on elsebody's house.

Dreaming in tears.
The flowers on the case getting their salty
Quench. Tainted.

Living through tears.
Eyes half empty.

So I'll climb the hill she's not yet over
And scream at the city that
We can't sleep in.

Chapel

There are candles. I
Lift one
From the bowl and place it, single
So careful in the second bowl, floating.

The matches are long, as if they will burn
For longer, but
The draught from the airtight entrance
Encourages it.
Rushes it.
The wick becomes
From the first,
And then
Original flame
Fades,
Diminishing and then leaving
The new flame to fill the whole bowl
With light.
But the rim is too far,
And the flowers that accompany in aesthetic are
    obstacles,
And I fear that a wave will
Extinguish her.

The Cusp of Spring

Coiled buds.
Waiting beauty,
So much new life when the ripping of lives
Is ignored.
Not heard
Like the cries and the sobs I will not let myself make,
And the counsel I will not take.

And the songs I know I cannot sing
Through the slow suffocation of a sigh.

Dinner

Dad keeping us from silence,
We keeping him from solace.

Escapism

I stand on the verge of
The county.
The distance in the hills becoming the
Blue of the sky.
The fog the clouds
Of a British anytime.

If it would roll over me,
Like the fictional coincidence of weather,
The aptness,
The thunder inside would
Rock me.

Evasion

Stay awake, don't rest your head,
Don't remember that she's dead.
While her soul drifts in the skies,
Stay awake, don't close your eyes.

Fourteen Days

The tears slide the wrong way down my face
Ruining the moisturiser routine.
Salt eats at my cheeks,
Chafing the patches of
Child-soreness,
Bitemarks which the wind has left.

The words have not come for a fortnight
Even
Now they fal-ter.

The familiar sting around the lies
The eyes
Where the liner once lay.
The sting secondary to that in the bridge
Of the nose
And before those in the diaphragm.
As if I have sung a symphony,

Emotion with only pitch.

In the Madness Between Sleep...

And wake
The blossoms have formed.
And the rain of life
Strews my pavement
On my once-again walk.
They punctuate the banality.

You never do know how dry the world has been
Until the rains come to quench the soil,
Drench the dust from its hovering,
Making it taste.

Rivulets form down my parched face,
As if there is a sea.

You never do realise just how dead
The world has been
Until the blossoms fall
Like the darkness
Which you did not notice
Until the blinding scar
Of life breaks through after so long.

Last Dance

Dancing the last dance beneath the lovers' gaze,
Making the steps,
Muscle memory making up for the
Amnesia of a heart
Eyes reflecting
With a mourner's glaze.
Varnished into the hue of
The coping soul.

Last Question

Trust you to pick the more complicated synonym.
Poetic words from your sermons.
Ignite, not light;
Extinguish, not blow out.

My last joy that it was already lit
And floating,
Along the passage,
Where you would believe he would be watching.
You answered my questions
Like a child
Who has had the questions answered for her
All her life.

Maternity

The longing of my heart for you
Is the yearning
Of my arms for that babe
I have not had.
My crook feeling already the weight of a tiny
Heavy
Love. My hands
Remember how it was to clasp around you tightly,
Close to you,
Limp by my sides,
My unstretched hips.

Memories Tainted

The setting is always
That one-way
White-washed cave,
The décor bleeding into your face,
Dragging you away…

My dreams paint you true:
In colour;
In life.
At waking, the limits of history steal you again
Again
The wan sepia of ancestors.

The ultra-clean linoleum
Of the single corridor,
With its branches
And the slight slope up to the chapel,
Will not show your reflection,
Because You are already gone.
Just like you asked.

Ode to a Helium Heart Lost Above Exeter

It was St Valentine's day yesterday.
I slept through half
And
Try-not-to-cry-ed
For the rest.

Post-Mortem

I watched the trees bronze in the 8pm sun,
May wiping golden linings onto the spring greens.
Gilt with the promise of summer.

A single shot
Of bounty and life and
Chlorophyll falling to dusk
As each gold leaf hovers
Over the valley.

A single shot
That I hoped the barman;
Would slide
Like in the olden movies;

A single shot
That would ring out
Ricocheting across the
Valley
With bagatelle intention;

A single shot
That held all five smiles
And hers the wonkiest
And her silly showing through;

A single shot
To break this membrane
And gasp for the life
That she has not nourished
And that feels so cold
And so bright on my
Shining vein-ed eyes.

Return

I find myself wishing
My life five years
Away,
Hoping for the blurry film of hindsight,
For the numb of time,
The loss of memory.

Solstice

When thinking slips into dreaming slips into waking
And realising that a part of my love is missing.
In the pre-spring-forward dawn,
The nearly light of the day
Marching
Like the hordes of Narcissi that friends have lit my
   little life with.

The beating of a heart
With one less ventricle
Takes a while to realise the rhythm
Of a day with three or four doorways.
Cross-rhythms of a gasp less.

Stages of Bereavement

A certain number of weeks after,
I had a compulsion to watch *Bambi*.
The masochism of grief.

A Sunday in April

Today, Dear Diary, Agony Aunt,
Etc., I feel pretty fucking destructive.
And the ripples I thought I could contain
Have formed a salty tsunami.

You have so much to live for
Enjoy yourself and what's more
You can grow
With so much to give for
Deep within your core
You must go
And be you

Fred's Lyrics

Preface

Fred has written hundreds of songs and was at his most prolific during his episodes of mental illness. Here are a few of the lyrics he wrote.

Dancing Free

Scampering around in circles feeling lost
This head-wind has certainly come at a high cost!
My clothes a mess, my hair a state
Why can't fashion and weather be best mates?

Feeling like I've been turned upside down in one fell
    swoop
I don't want to sell my soul out of a car-boot
Feeling misguided, misdirected, confused
But in the end I'll pull through

And to escape from the rat race
What a way to live with a human trace!
They all want to stand out, be bold, magnanimous
I just want some change for when I catch the bus

And I want to go outside and be free,
Not worry about all that's been bothering me
To act as I want to, act my age
Not emotionally trapped within a cage

Dancing free

Happiness

Happiness – something I've come to know
Had sadness, I was in bed
Now I get up – I feel the sunshine here instead

I felt lost and I felt low
I was trapped and I was cold

Oh yeah
Mmm hmm

Happiness – something I've come to know
Falling apart at the seams
My life was a series of broken dreams and dread

Sometimes lost and sometimes low
Baffled, confused, nowhere to go

Oh yeah
Mmm hmm

Happiness – something I've come to know
If you make the most of your life you can smile
You can grow and then regrow

Happiness – something I've come to know

Oh yeah
Mmm hmm

Happiness – something I've come to know

Love's Inside the Heart

I believe that love's inside the heart
I believe in love
I believe that we can make a start
To embrace our world with love

So I walked to the shops and I found it quite trying
But I got there okay
I came back and felt like crying
But I overcame the pain

So I strolled in the park and found it quite a challenge
But I got on okay
When I was in the park I thought, 'This needs more
    flowers
Because it could be great.' Yeah, it could be great

Then I came home and I couldn't stop eating
And I felt like going to bed
I felt so scared, like a victim of scheming
But it was all in my head

I felt so confused, searching for meaning
Not sure what to do
The nasties run around yet they're still sleeping
With orders blind and blue

I believe that love's inside the heart
I believe in love
I believe that we can make a start
To embrace our world with love

So Much to Live For

Don't give up
Don't give up
You have so much to offer this world
You can enjoy yourself as well
Don't give up

Live in hope
Live in hope
Things can be better, you'll see
Improve for you and me
Live in hope

Smile, smile today
Smile, smile today
Don't give up

You have so much to live for
Enjoy yourself and what's more
You can grow
With so much to give for
Deep within your core
You must go
And be you
And be you

Find yourself
Find yourself
You may not know what you want yet
But be creative
You'll find yourself

You make a whole
You make a whole
Just keep open-minded
And yet becoming
You'll find your soul

Play some music today
For yourself and your sanity
It's here to heal
It's here for real

You have so much to live for
Enjoy yourself and what's more
You can grow
With so much to give for
Deep within your core
You must go
And be you,
And be you.

My five-year-old son runs in to
the end of the room,
Mounts the step and turns,
Grinning in triumph.

Andrew's Poem

Preface

Andrew has written many poems. The following he wrote about his father's suicide, many years after the event.

Redemption

African summer –
Jacaranda blossoms popping underfoot,
Violet on the blue-slate stoep.

I'm seventeen –
Buried in the heart of sweltering suburbia,
Frantically cramming for school-leaving exams.

One airless night,
My mother wakes to find her bed empty
For the first time in twenty-five years.
Her voice as she shakes me, taut with concern –
"I can't find Dad."

We search the house, then the garden,
Honeysuckle heavy on the humid air.

Peering into the swimming pool
I know something is badly wrong.

One place remains –
An outbuilding, the workshop where my father
Relieved the fine-motor tension of the surgeon's craft
By beating sheets of copper into bowls.

I try the locked door,
Smash the window,
Climb in, turn on the lights.

At the far end a step leads to a washroom
Behind a door, tight shut;
The step awash with my father's blood.

I turn away and walk outside,
My mother keening at the open door.

Thirty years later, with my own family,
I travel the six thousand miles
To my hometown.

A visit to our old house nearly ends
Outside a high wall warning:
'Armed Response'.

Over the intercom I explain
Who I am and what I want.
The African caretaker, alone in charge,
Decides to let us in.

The owners away, the house is locked.
He shows us round the garden.
The brick barbecue my father built,
The swimming pool, the mulberry tree we used to climb
Are all still there.

The tour ends
By the workshop where my father died.
Without explanation, our guide
Unlocks the door and swings it open.

My five-year-old son runs in to the end of the room,
Mounts the step and turns,
Grinning in triumph.

A double exposure, two images overlap –
The bloody step and a child's smiling face.
Then the first shot fades, leaving just my lovely son
And a line drawn under all my guilt –

That I could have done more:
During that night I'd half-woken,
Heard the gentle thud of the twelve-bore
Swinging against the inside of the cupboard door
Where it always hung, in its green canvas bag,
In case of an emergency.

The crisis is acute: mental health is an appallingly neglected area of need in twenty-first-century Britain...

Constructing a healthy mental health agenda can be part of a broader attempt at building a fundamentally more caring and supportive society, which alleviates the causes of mental distress.

Afterword

The Size of the Problem

One in four people in the UK are known to suffer from a mental health problem at some point in their lives, but millions of mentally ill people go untreated and unsupported. 43% of adults at some time think that they have had a diagnosable mental health condition but only 19.5% of men and 33.7% of women have had these diagnoses confirmed by professionals. 10–15% of new mothers experience post-natal depression; 90% of prisoners have a diagnosed mental health problem; and many ex-soldiers suffer from post-traumatic stress.

Mental health problems are the most commonly cited cause of absence from work.[2] NHS hospitals in England now admit twice as many drug-related mental health problems as compared to ten years ago. (These drugs include cannabis and cocaine, painkillers, alcohol and solvents.)[3] And mentally ill people are acutely disturbed by lives of stress, trauma,

2. https://www.mentalhealth.org.uk/sites/default/files/fundamental-facts-about-mental-health-2016.pdf
3. https://www.theguardian.com/society/2018/mar/03/admissions-to-hospital-for-drug-related-mental-health-problems-soar

poverty, poor housing, abusive relationships, homelessness and unemployment.

But do our mental health services meet the challenges we face? They barely scratch the surface. The life stories in this book show first-hand evidence that our mental health services are inadequate. There are staff shortages and clearly insufficient training. In 2016 the government stated an intention to put money into the mental health system after six years of cuts and neglect. But in 2017 Marjorie Wallace, chief executive of the mental health charity Sane, said that despite much campaigning 'cuts to services across the country continue and people seeking help are still being failed.' She highlighted a recent report which found that '40 per cent of the mental health trusts in England had seen cuts to their budgets' and that 'figures show mental health trusts received none of the extra £8bn funding for the NHS over the last four years.'[4] It seems that some politicians cynically use rhetoric to acknowledge shortcomings in mental health services while they simultaneously fail to address the massive funding and training deficit required to address the problem.

In an editorial piece in *Mind & Memory* Rachael Linkie observed:

Official figures released early this year, for instance, show that mental health patients are still being forced to travel hundreds of miles for care due to bed shortages. Many experts have warned that being split from families for long periods causes 'significant psychological damage'.

---

4   https://www.independent.co.uk/news/health/mental-health-nhs-funding-cut-millions-five-england-regions-1-billion-spent-2021-scarborough-walsall-a7700476.html by Katie Forster, Tuesday 25 April 2017.

So, the mental health system is failing us and little is being done by the government to address their scandalous shortcomings. Mental health should be given the same priority as physical health, especially as this is an issue that affects so many of us.

The crisis is acute: people with mental health needs are amongst the most vulnerable in society and yet mental health is an appallingly neglected area of need in twenty-first-century Britain.

What Can Be Done

Developing awareness of what it is like to have mental health challenges is important because it helps us to better identify and understand the issue. But we also need to campaign – for better funding for mental health hospitals, halfway houses, and staffing, for decent hospital food, and more beds, and for employment schemes that pay aspiring workers challenged by mental health challenges with accumulative levels of responsibility. We need more staff, trained more holistically – medically, socially and psychologically, and staff need better pay. Better pay would attract more staff and better paid staff means happier staff, means happier service users, and happier service users mean a happier society.

We need more frequent and more therapeutic mental health residential provision and far more community provision. We need free online, work and school-based meditation and relaxation programmes. Better training requires holistic grounding in physical, biological and social factors, and knowledge of the impact of a range of medications. The scale and funding required may seem awesome but surely the huge-scale government funding that is currently secured for wars that kill (which in themselves create a multitude of mental health problems) could be better spent constructively helping people to *survive* and lead healthy lives.

The world may seem an aggressive place full of prejudice, suffering and division. If we are to rise to the challenge of making it better this means that we should support our most vulnerable people, their families and friends, and the institutions and individuals that are required to care for them. It means building a society where mental distress is less prevalent and so address today's crisis. Constructing a healthy mental health agenda can be part of a broader attempt at building a fundamentally more caring and supportive society, which alleviates the causes of mental distress in the first place.

I hope you found this book useful for helping you, or someone you know, to better understand and cope with the mental health challenges you/they face, that it increases your knowledge of various issues, and helps shine a little light on dark days and forward on the road to recovery, for individuals and society.

Appendices 1: Glossary

Here are the meanings of some commonly used mental health terms.

Mental Health Challenges

Anxiety disorders – The most common of all mental illnesses, anxiety disorders are a manifestation of intense anxiety and/ or worry. Conditions include generalised anxiety disorder, obsessive-compulsive disorder, panic disorder, phobias, post-traumatic stress disorder and separation anxiety. In 2013 there were 8.2 million cases of anxiety in the UK.[5]

Symptoms include feelings of fear and/or worry that are difficult to control and which interfere with normal activities, panic attacks, an overall sense of unease and specific fears such as being on an aeroplane, in a crowd or in the dark.

Bipolar disorder – Formerly known as manic depression, this involves extreme changes in mood – from high states of mania to low states of depression. Affects 1–2% of people. In

---

5.   https://www.mentalhealth.org.uk/statistics/mental-health-statistics-anxiety

2013 nearly 4 million people in the UK were diagnosed with bipolar disorder including 3.4% of 16-24-year-olds and 0.4% of 65-74-year-olds.[6]

It can occur during or after pregnancy for women.

Symptoms of mania include abnormal and continuous highs, being happy or euphoric, or irritable, angry or aggressive, exaggerated self-esteem, less need for sleep, increased talking, racing thoughts, hyperactivity and poor judgement.

Depressive states may include low mood, loss of interest in pleasure or activities one used to find enjoyable, weight loss or gain, insomnia or oversleeping, apathy or agitation, loss of energy, feelings of guilt or worthlessness, difficulty concentrating and suicidal thoughts.

Clinical depression – Also known as major depressive disorder, this is a complex mood disorder marked by intense melancholy, weakness, demotivation, and sometimes a sense of uselessness.

One type of depression is seasonal affective disorder (SAD), which is affected by weather and time of year. Clinical depression can occur alongside psychosis as with bipolar disorder when someone can lose touch with reality.

Clinical depression affects 10% of men and 5% of women.

Symptoms include feelings of hopelessness, inadequacy, loss of interest, and difficulty in performing everyday tasks.

Depression can affect sleep, appetite, energy levels, concentration, memory, motivation and decision-making. It can give rise to suicidal thoughts and numbness to things that usually cause pleasure. Everyday tasks like washing, cooking, and going to work may become difficult and lead to other emotional or physical problems.

6. https://www.mentalhealth.org.uk/statistics/mental-health-statistics-bipolar

First episode of psychosis – This is the first time someone experiences an extreme loss of contact with reality, sometimes with difficulty in distinguishing what is real and what is not. Often frightening, confusing and distressing, such episodes usually first appear in someone's late teens or early twenties.

Low energy problem (LEP) – Intense lethargy, tiredness and depressive states. Includes irregular sleeping patterns or lack of sleep.

Nervous breakdown – An intense experience of mental distress where normal mental functioning is impaired. May be triggered by depression, anxiety, psychosis, hormonal changes or stress.

Signs of a breakdown may include not eating/sleeping enough or too little, poor hygiene, intense depression, intense mental activity, missing days from work and isolating oneself at home.

Personality disorder – A condition which comprises a long-term pattern of behaviour which deviates from the norm where someone thinks, feels, behaves or relates to others in society in an atypical fashion. Usually starting in adolescence, personality disorder can cause long-term difficulties in personal relationships and social functioning.

5% of the population of the UK are diagnosed with one of ten types of personality disorder.[7] These types include borderline personality disorder, antisocial personality disorder, narcissistic personality disorder, paranoid personality disorder and obsessive-compulsive personality disorder and each type has different symptoms.

Symptoms of borderline personality disorder include

---

7.   http://personalitydisorder.org.uk/borderline-personality-disorder/

marked reactivity, paranoia, unstable self-image, changeable intense relationships, suicidal gestures, inappropriate anger, frantic efforts to avoid real or imagined abandonment and chronic feelings of emptiness.

Having several of the above symptoms means that someone may have a personality disorder but if these symptoms go into remission, the person will be said to no longer have personality disorder.

Post-Natal depression – This type of depression is suffered by mothers following childbirth, often arising from a combination of hormonal changes, psychological adjustment to motherhood, and fatigue. It is also known as postpartum depression. Affects one in ten mothers.

Post-Traumatic Stress Disorder - A type of anxiety disorder that emerges following traumatic events, often war trauma. Delayed-onset PTSD is when symptoms emerge more than six months after experiencing trauma; complex PTSD is when someone experiences trauma at an early age or lasting for a long time; and birth trauma develops following a traumatic experience of giving birth.

Symptoms include distressing flashbacks, difficulty in remembering things, feelings of numbness and trouble sleeping.[8]

Psychosis or psychotic disorder – A mental disorder in which thought and emotions are impaired so that an individual develops fears of persecution beyond their likelihood in external reality.

The disorder may be brief psychotic disorder (one day to

---

8.   https://www.mind.org.uk/information-support/types-of-mental-health-problems/post-traumatic-stress-disorder-ptsd/about-ptsd/

one month), schizophreniform disorder (one to six months), delusional disorder (with non-bizarre delusions but without hallucinations, negative symptoms, disorganised speech or behaviour) or schizoaffective disorder (two weeks or longer psychosis followed by psychosis with low mood).

Symptoms include hallucinations (hearing voices or seeing things that are not really there), paranoia and having ideas not based in reality.

Puerperal psychosis – A type of mental illnesses that follow childbirth, involving a sudden onset of psychotic symptoms. May include irritability, extreme mood swings and hallucinations.

Schizophrenia – A mental disorder that involves a breakdown in the relation between thought, emotion, and behaviour.

Schizophrenia is a manifestation of psychosis.

It can last for at least six months, although with anti-psychotic medication its intensity can diminish over time.

Can include faulty perception, inappropriate actions and feelings, withdrawal from reality and personal relationships into fantasy, delusion and a sense of mental fragmentation.

Symptoms include hallucinations (hearing voices or seeing), delusions, inability to perform everyday tasks, high or low levels of the brain chemical dopamine which can affect one's judgement and disorganised speech or behaviour.

Thought disorder - This is a psychotic, cognitive illness where thoughts and conversation appear illogical, lacking in sequence and/or are delusional or bizarre.

Drugs

Anti-anxiety medications
Benzodiazepines: alprazolam (under brand name Xanax), chlordiazepoxide (Librium), clonazepam (Klonopin), diazepam (Valium), lorazepam (Ativan) and oxazepam (Serax).
Beta-blockers: atenolol (Tenormin) and propranolol (Inderal).

Anti-depressant medications
SSRIs: citalopram (Celexa, Cipramil), escitalopram (Lexapro), fluoxetine (Prozac), paroxetine (Paxil, Pexeva, Seroxat), sertraline (Zoloft), vilazodone (Viibryd).
SSNRIs: desvenlafaxine (Khedezla, Pristiq), duloxetine (Cymbalta, Irenka), levomilnacipran (Fetzima), milnacipran (Savella), venlafaxine (Effexor).

Anti-psychotic/schizophrenia medications (also called neuroleptics)
Newer anti-psychotics: amisulpride (or for bipolar mania, Solian), aripiprazole (Abilify), clozapine (Clozaril, Denzapine, Zaponex), lurasidone (Latuda), olanzapine (Zypadhera, Zyprexa), paliperidone (Invega, Xeplion), quetiapine (Seroquel, Seroquel XL), risperidone (Risperidal, Risperdal Consta).
Older antipsychotics: benperidol (Anquil), chlorpromazine, droperidol (Inapsine), flupentixol (Depixol and Fluanxol), fluphenazine (Modecate, Proloxin) [from 2018 no longer in use], haloperidol (Haldol), levomepromazine (Detenler, Hirnamin,

Levoprome, Levotmin, Neurocil, Nozinan), loxapine (Loxitane), pericyazine (Neulactil), pimozide (Orap), prochlorperazine (Compro), promazine (Sparine), sulpiride (Dogmatil), trifluoperazine (Stelazine), zuclopenthixol (Cisordinol, Clopixol, Acuphase).

Mood Stabilisers
Divalproex sodium (Depakote), lithium carbonate (Eskalith, Eskalith-Cr, Lithane, Lithobid, Lithonate, Lithotabs).

Psychotropic prescription – medication that affects the mind, emotions, and behaviour.

SNRIs and SSRIs: serotonin and norepinephrine reuptake inhibitors, and selective serotonin reuptake inhibitors are used for treating depression and anxiety disorders. SNRIs block the reabsorption of both serotonin and norepinephrine, while SSRIs solely affect serotonin levels.

For queries about medications and conditions contact your GP, psychiatrist and/or local mental health services.

People, Places and Organisations

Birmingham Disorder Research Network – The world's largest network of people with bipolar disorder and related mood disorders.

Care worker – Someone who provides support and supervises vulnerable or disadvantaged people.

Cognitive Behavioural Therapy (CBT) – A talking therapy that analyses the relationship between a patient's thoughts, beliefs and attitudes, CBT is deployed to help people manage their problems by enabling them to change how they think and behave.

It can be used for treating different conditions from anxiety and depression to other mental health challenges. Work with a CBT therapist may help disrupt negative thought cycles, and help generate more positive ones.

CDAT team – Stands for Complex Depression Anxiety and Trauma service. Run by local council or mental health teams.

Consultant – This is someone who provides expert advice professionally.

Community Psychiatric Nurses (CPN) – Psychiatric nurses who are based in the community rather than in psychiatric hospital. They may be part of 'Crisis' Teams or work independently.

'Crisis' Team – A group of mental health workers including social workers, CPNs, psychiatrists and psychologists, who provide care in the community for individuals who are 'in crisis', with suicidal thoughts, clinical depression, anxiety disorders, psychosis and/or at risk to themselves/others. They also help to make assessments in A & E departments in hospitals.

'Halfway' House – A place within which people with mental, emotional or physical disabilities, sometimes with criminal backgrounds, are supported, where they can learn skills for reintegration into society. These houses may provide social, medical, psychiatric, therapeutic and educational support.

Key worker – For people with mental health challenges to talk to, providing support. Co-ordinate care in contact with different professionals and may offer counselling.

Maudsley hospital – A large NHS mental health service based in south London that particularly works with families. It provides the largest mental health training institution in the UK and works with the Institute of Psychiatry at King's College London.

MIND – A large NHS mental health charity that provides information and advice to people with mental health problems. It also lobbies government and local authorities on behalf of service users, striving for support and respect.

The National Autistic Society – This is the UK's leading charity for people affected by autism. It provides information, support and services.

Outpatient doctors – NHS workers that support people in the community.

The Priory – A group of private hospitals that provide mental health rehabilitation, education and care.

Psychiatrist – Medical practitioners that diagnose and treat mental distress. Psychiatrists can prescribe medication, which psychologists cannot do.

Psychoanalyst – Mental health professionals that treat mental health distress and problems by looking to the relationship between conscious and unconscious elements in the mind.

Psychologist – Professionals specialising in diagnosing and treating mental health distress, using talk therapies.

Rethink – Mental health charity that provides supportive advice and services, and campaigns for people with mental distress.

Service user – Another word for patients of (mental) health services.

Social worker – Provide community-based support for people with mental health challenges. Ideally they will enable individuals to develop skills to use their own resources to solve problems.

Other

Beck Questionaire – A series of multi-choice questions developed by Aaron T Beck, widely used for measuring the severity of depression.

ECT – Electroconvulsive Therapy is a procedure where small electric currents are passed through the brain, causing changes in brain chemistry to reverse symptoms of mental distress such as clinical depression.

Endogenous – This means having internal cause/origin.

Neuroscience – The study of how the nervous system develops, its structure, and what it does, looking at the brain and its impact on behaviour and cognitive functions.

Sectioning – When someone is compulsorily legally committed to a psychiatric hospital in accordance with a section of a mental health act. This assessment is done by a doctor.

Ward round – When a hospital doctor visits the impatients in a hospital ward.

Appendices 2: Useful Websites

Listed below are links to some key mental health services.

BNF (British National Formulary) and NICE (the National Institute for Health and Care Excellence) An informative website on medications for mental and physical health. Very useful.

https://bnf.nice.org.uk

CALM (Campaign Against Living Miserably)
A charity dedicated to the prevention of male suicide, offering guidance and support. It seems to offer a similar service to the Samaritans, but for men only. It is more active in some areas of the country than others and has limited resources and depth of help, but provides useful advice for what to do when someone you know may be suicidal.

thecalmzone.net

Carers UK
A long-established health charity that provides help and

advice, and campaigns for carers. The website has useful advice about allowances and governmental financial benefits, but limited resources related to mental distress.

carersuk.org/

Community Advice and Listening Line
Offers emotional support and information on mental health and related matters to people in Wales.

callhelpline.org.uk

DPAC (Disabled People Against Cuts)
Campaigns for justice and human rights for disabled people. Its Facebook page is informative on campaigning issues.

dpac.uk.net

Headspace
Provides effective meditation to promote mental wellbeing (ideally listened to with headphones). Helps people with a range of conditions. Initially free. Some contributors to this book enjoyed using this.

https://www.headspace.com

Inspire (Irish Association for Mental Health)
Provides local services to support the mental health and wellbeing for people in the island of Ireland, as well as students in Scotland.

inspirewellbeing.org

Mental Health Foundation
A huge, established mental health charity providing guidance on mental health problems, topical issues and treatments.

mentalhealth.org.uk

MIND

An established charity, MIND provides a comprehensive website with information, support, news and campaigns, blogs (such as that below) featuring individuals' experiences with different conditions, experiences and medications. It is more in-depth and wider-ranging in its support than CALM. Also provides local mental health services on a commissionary basis.

mind.org.uk/information-support/your-stories/living-with-depression-my-experience/

Mindfulness

There are many online mindfulness videos and exercises freely available such as those on YouTube.

NHS

The NHS provides a vast A–Z resource on health, living well, care and support, health news, and local services.

www.nhs.uk/Conditions/Depression/Pages/living-with.aspx

A five-point plan for good mental health.

www.nhs.uk/Conditions/stress-anxiety-depression/Pages/improve-mental-wellbeing.aspx

Medications.

https://www.nhs.uk/conditions/ssri-antidepressants/

Dorset Healthcare's Mental Health webpages provide support for children and adults with many useful for coping strategies for a wide range of conditions.

wheresyourheadat.co.uk

Psychologists for Social Change

A network of psychologists, academics, graduates and others interested in applying psychology to policy and progressive political action.

psychchange.org

Also see Against Austerity's Facebook page.

Rethink

A campaigning mental health charity originally focusing on schizophrenia, now extends more broadly into mental health.

rethink.org

The **Royal College of Psychiatrists** website provides information on medications for mental distress. A very informative website for mental health professionals.

https://www.rcpsych.ac.uk/mental-health/treatments-and-wellbeing

Samaritans

Provides information on 'trigger situations' and 'things you can do to help yourself', as well as providing support for those in need. Their phone line is particularly useful when service users have clinical depression.

https://www.samaritans.org/how-we-can-help/support-and-information/if-youre-having-difficult-time/signs-you-may-be-struggling-cope/ or phone 116123

Young Minds

Offers information, support and advice for children and young people.

youngminds.org.uk

Appendices 3: Useful Books

Listed below are links to some books that you might find helpful:

Happy: 50 Mindfulness and Relaxation Exercises To Boost Your Mood Every Day by Dr Alene K Unger (Quantam Books, 2016). Provides easy exercises to minimise negative thoughts and encourages a positive, joyful outlook.

Henry's Demons: A Father and Son's Journey Out of Madness by Patrick and Henry Cockburn (Simon & Schuster, 2011). First-hand account of a young man living with symptoms of schizophrenia. Co-authored by an established journalist, it is harrowing and important.

Mental Health by Jeremy Weinstein (Policy Press, 2014). Critical reading about radical social work.

Psychology and Capitalism: the Manipulation of Mind by Ron Roberts (Zero Books, 2015). Reveals how modern society causes mental distress. May be a little challenging for those suffering with paranoid symptoms.

Reasons to Stay Alive by Matt Haig (Canongate, 2015). One man's heart-warming story of overcoming the obstacles of mental distress.

Various helpful booklets on different mental health conditions have been published by MIND.